MAKE TODAY COUNT

MAKE TODAY COUNT

ORVILLE E. KELLY
with Randall Becker

Foreword by
Elisabeth Kübler-Ross

Delacorte Press / New York

Manufactured in the United States of America
Second Printing—1975

LIBRARY OF CONGRESS CATALOGING IN PUBLICATION DATA

Kelly, Orville, 1930-
Make today count.

1. Cancer—Personal narratives. 2. Kelly, Orville, 1930- I. Becker, Randall, joint author. II. Title.
RC263.K43 362.1'9'699400924 {B} 75-17813

ISBN *0-440-05256-4*

Everything in this book is true.
In some cases, however, names, dates,
and places have been changed
to protect the privacy
of people involved.

A SPECIAL THANKS

to Dr. Carl Hulen, Dr. Don Winter,
and all the medical staff at the hospitals
in Burlington and Iowa City . . .
to Jeanne Kuster—a real mainstay of
Make Today Count . . .
to Nancy E. Gross of Dell
Publishing Co., for her aid
and friendship . . .
and to those thousands of
cancer patients, many
now dead, who helped
light the tunnel.

DEDICATION

To my wife, Wanda,
and our children, Mark, Tammy, Lori, and Britty ..
without whose love and understanding
I could not have turned my life around.
When I am with them, the sun shines
a little brighter and the roses
smell more fragrant.

FOREWORD

I looked for my soul
but my soul I could not see.
I looked for my God
but my God eluded me.
I looked for a friend
and then I found all three.

"Orville Kelly is dying of cancer." So began a newspaper article about the author of this book. Yes, Orville *is* dying. And so are you. So are all of you who read these pages and all of us who have been privileged to know Orville and Wanda and all the many people who have made this book possible.

Millions of people live an everyday life—they pursue their interests, earn a living, pay taxes, and take a few weeks' vacation to "get away from it all" or have a little time to get to know their family. We eat, drink, sleep, work, and run around; and we take it all too much for granted.

Then one day, you or I have some pain and we try to ignore it. We try to forget that it does not respond; we label it as "arthritis" or "a virus" when the fatigue and tiredness do not disappear. And sooner or later we have to hear the news: "It is malignant."

It is at this point in our life that we are suddenly reminded that we have a limited life span, that we may not be able to postpone things any longer, that there may not always be a tomorrow.

Too many people live in the illusion that patients do not know when they are terminally ill. Too many relatives play a game, pretend that all is well. Little do they appreciate that it is this very awareness of our limited life span that gives us the courage to fight, the strength to carry on, the wisdom to use each day as a gift, and the ability to say "I love you" before it is too late.

The strength, courage, and wisdom that evolve from times of pain and suffering cannot come forth when we are left alone and isolated. It will not be able to blossom when we are faced with people who avoid us or the issue of our dying. It can come forth only if we have a friend who is willing to share this time with us; who can sit and listen; who does not take off when we need to cry; who understands our agony and our fears; and who is willing to hold our hand when we can no longer speak.

Orville has made this possible through his own experience. He has started to light a candle in the darkness, and within a few months, candles have started to burn all over the country; candles of friendship, compassion, and love among people who know that we have to *Make Today Count* because no one knows if we can still do it tomorrow.

I hope that the light he has brought into the darkness will shine for him and for Wanda to the last moment of his earthly existence and that he will know it will shine even brighter afterward.

Elisabeth Kübler-Ross

ONE

The appointment was set for nine o'clock that morning.

It was Friday, June 15, 1973. In two days it would be Father's Day, but no one in our family was discussing that. My wife, Wanda, and our four children were too concerned about me. And so was I—concerned not only about myself, but also about the problems I seemed to be bringing on them. At four in the morning I woke in a cold sweat from a nightmare that had pursued me for two nights now. I was lying in a casket, and my family was passing by me for the last time.

The sun seemed to wait for hours before popping up over the Mississippi River. I lay in bed, waiting for daylight—tired, nervous, and, above all, scared. I was forty-two years old. I had a family I loved and that loved me. It should have been the prime of my life. But it was far from that.

The trouble had begun about a year and a half earlier, when we were living in Aledo, a town in western Illinois, and I was managing editor of the weekly newspaper. We'd been there only a few months and had just about settled into the big white house with its front yard for the children to play in and its back porch for our barbecues, when I came down with a pneumonia so severe that it had me in the hospital twice and away from work for more than three months.

By late that year, it had become apparent that I couldn't keep up with the rigorous demands of a weekly publication schedule, and I began to look for easier work. But even when I found a job that made fewer demands on my strength, I couldn't cope with it. At times, I was so exhausted that I literally couldn't get out of bed in the mornings. And there was the pain in my knees—sometimes so sharp that I couldn't stand up straight. Part of the problem, according to the doctors, was high uric acid in my system. But—so one doctor told Wanda, sternly—most of it was in my head.

Wherever the problem was, it had, by September of 1972, become really acute. I wasn't well enough to hold down any kind of steady job, no matter how simple. My medical expenses had mounted astronomically. We were down to our last $150 when we decided to head for Burlington, Iowa, where

Wanda's parents lived and where I had lived for a time as a child.

For a while, things seemed a little better. The three oldest children began school; I worked at an occasional odd job; and Wanda became the breadwinner, taking a job in an electronics factory. I certainly wasn't happy about that; after all, it was my role to support my family. But we were still together; we were still a family. And early in 1972, the opportunity came for me to attend an office training school in Des Moines, about two hundred miles northwest of Burlington. There I hoped to acquire some skills that would enable me to earn a living for my family without putting too heavy a strain on my strength. I took a room at the local YMCA, and set to work studying. But when the day of the graduation ceremony dawned, my legs hurt so much that I couldn't get out of bed. The pain was so severe that I couldn't even get to a phone to call the doctor—although I'm far from sure any doctor would have made a house call to the YMCA. It wasn't until several days later that, with the help of a friend, I was able to make it down to the bus station to take the two-hundred-mile trip back home. By the time I got to Burlington, I felt so weak and was in such pain that I literally had to crawl up the stairs to my bedroom.

Then one morning in April of 1973, while I was

shaving, I felt a lump under my left arm. A few days later, I found another, right next to the first one. And a few days thereafter, a third appeared, in my groin. The third one really frightened me, and I went to a doctor.

He looked, palpated it, and smiled reassuringly. "It's nothing to worry about," he said. "They're probably only fatty tumors."

I was relieved, but not entirely convinced. Daily I seemed to be feeling weaker, and I hadn't been able to work for more than a month. But if the doctor said there was nothing to worry about, I would try not to worry.

By June, however, it was impossible not to worry. Things were getting worse, not better. I finally made an appointment to see another local doctor. This man was far less optimistic than his colleague had been. It might very well be something serious, he said. Indeed, he suspected lymphoma—cancer of the lymph glands. The only way to find out was to have one of the tumors removed, for examination. He urged me not to delay.

Now my day at the hospital had arrived. I finally crawled out of bed, took a bath, and got dressed—I wore, I remember, a white shirt, black slacks, and a blue sports coat. Wanda was downstairs making breakfast for the children. When she came upstairs to dress, her face was tense and drawn. But all I could manage to say to her was, "Don't worry."

By 8:45, Tammy and Lori had left for school, the baby-sitter had arrived to take care of Britty, and Wanda's mother, Lora, was waiting downstairs with our oldest son, thirteen-year-old Mark, who wanted to come to the hospital with us. So the four of us climbed into our yellow 1969 Ford for the seven-minute drive to Burlington Memorial Hospital.

None of us spoke during those seven minutes. I stared out the window, seeing nothing but the overcast sky and trying not to think ahead by thinking back—back to happy times our family had had together. There was the summer we had taken off, the whole Kelly tribe, a camper attached to the back of our car, for a trip westward. There we were, somewhere in Nebraska, on Interstate 80 at sunrise of a shiny day, with the strains of Bob Dylan's "Hey, Mr. Tambourine Man" on our cartridge player. There was the shopping trip we had all made in Itasca, Illinois, in 1969. I had just begun a reporting job with a suburban newspaper chain. Wanda was pregnant with Britty. I was pushing a cart in the grocery store, and Wanda and the three children tagged along behind as we prepared to stock our new home with groceries.

But now I was in the heart of downtown Burlington, as we approached the four-story hospital building. The parking spaces in front of the hospital were filled, so Wanda let me out of the car at the main hospital entrance while she parked the car in a lot around the corner. I tried to act casual as I walked into the hospital and checked in at the main desk. Whether I succeeded or not, I don't know. But hospital people must be used to fear and to all the efforts we make to conceal it.

I filled out the necessary forms and took the elevator to the second floor, where the operating room was. It was small and gloomy, dominated by the high white table standing in the center of the room. I undressed and changed into a clumsy white gown, and the nurse helped me onto the operating table. By the time the doctor arrived, I was a little groggy from the pill I had been given, but I managed to exchange hellos with him. His voice is usually soft and reassuring, but that's not the way it sounded to me that day.

One of the nurses moved my left arm past my head and applied a local anesthetic to the area underneath my arm. I had specifically asked that only a local anesthetic be used. The fear of death had been with me for a long time now, and I was terrified that death would come to me during the operation if I wasn't awake and conscious the whole time.

I turned my head to the right and closed my eyes. I wanted to be awake—I wanted that desperately. But I did not want to have to watch the doctor at work. I could hear the doctor and nurses talking, but I couldn't always understand what they were saying. The operation was supposed to be relatively easy, but the doctor had a difficult time reaching the tumor.

"We're going to have to go deeper than we thought," I heard him say to one of the nurses. My stomach tightened, and I pressed my eyelids even more tightly together.

"Now we've got it," he said, and I turned my head to see a grayish-yellow mass of tissue about the size of a golf ball suspended at the end of the doctor's clamps.

"I'm looking at my death," I thought to myself. I closed my eyes and turned my head away from the rubbery ball hanging so menacingly above me.

I had just finished putting my clothes back on when the laboratory report came through. The doctor read it to me. It confirmed my most terrible fears: ". . . very large lymph node . . . proved the suspected diagnosis—malignant lymphoma . . ."

"It's bad, but that doesn't mean it's the end, you

know," the doctor said. "Now what we have to do is find out how advanced the cancer is. That will mean some further tests."

I stood there, unable to speak.

"Do you want us to bring your wife here," he asked, "so you can tell her?"

"I don't want to tell her. Will you do it?"

My voice must have sounded harsh and unfeeling. But I knew I couldn't face Wanda without breaking into tears. Tears for her and tears for myself, also. I had been pretty sure, all along, that something was seriously wrong with me. I had even suspected that I might remain a semi-invalid all my life. But cancer—that was a thought I couldn't bring myself to accept. Cancer didn't mean weakness and invalidism. Cancer meant death. It meant *my* death. No, it just couldn't be happening.

By this time, Wanda had come to the hallway outside the operating room, and the doctor left to talk to her. Out of the corner of my eye, I could see them conversing. I turned away; I didn't want to see. I was terrified and I was filled with fury. I wanted to strangle the doctor who had told me that the lumps were probably just fatty tumors, and the other doctor who had told Wanda that my problems were in my head. The nurse helped me button my shirt and then she put a sling around my left arm. I stood there for a moment and, gathering my courage together, slowly walked out to join Wanda. My eyes were beginning to brim with tears. I couldn't look at Wanda for fear I would cry. As we walked down the hall to the elevator, I kept my eyes glued to the floor. "Don't worry, I'm OK," I mumbled.

Wanda, Mark, and Lori walked to the car while I waited for them outside the hospital door. When Wanda pulled the car in front of me, I could see that she had been crying. I was afraid that if I talked to her, I would start crying too. But I pulled myself together.

"Don't worry about it, Wanda," I said, as if I could console her. "We've been through hard times before."

All of us were silent during the trip home. I was losing my life and my family, and I didn't know what to do or say. I had waited until I was twenty-nine years old to get married; but now I had Wanda, Mark, Tammy, Lori, and Britty. Wanda was only seventeen in 1959, when we were married, and even though we were both lost and confused when we met, we had stuck together through bad as well as good times, raising and nurturing a family we could call our own. And now I had cancer. I deserved more than that. I wanted to know why I was being shortchanged.

As soon as we got home, I headed straight for the den next to the dining room, closed the door, and lay down on the worn-out couch. I wanted to be alone. I couldn't speak to anyone.

But Wanda still had work to do. She had to take the baby-sitter home. The drive took almost fifteen minutes—fifteen minutes during which Wanda gritted her teeth and forced herself not to cry. When she had paid the baby-sitter and thanked her, she drove the car around the corner, pulled to the side of the road, laid her head on the steering wheel, and broke into tears.

Finally, she put the car in gear and started to drive home again, but the tears were still streaming from her eyes and her vision was blurred. Just two blocks from our home is St. John's Catholic Church. Wanda stopped the car there and slowly made her way into the church. Down the aisle she walked, and into the deserted chapel, lit only by the flickering candles at the side of the altar. After she walked past the rows of pews, she fell to her knees, looked up at the statue of Jesus hanging on the cross, and broke into tears. And she prayed.

Meanwhile, I wanted to know why I had been driven home to die.

My physician felt that additional testing should be conducted as soon as possible, so I was readmitted to Burlington Memorial early Sunday evening. During the day and a half I was at home, none of us spoke about my illness. If Wanda hadn't gone to the hospital with me, I would not have told her of the diagnosis. And even though she knew it, I could not bring myself to talk about it with her. I couldn't bring myself even to say the word "cancer." Mark was obviously as frightened of the word as I was. He had overheard Wanda telling her mother about the laboratory report when we were leaving the hospital, but he refused to believe her and angrily accused her of lying.

At the hospital I was placed, by coincidence, in the same room as an old friend, who had suffered a heart attack. When doctors and friends came to visit my roommate, they never seemed to be afraid to talk to him about his heart. But no one ever mentioned the word "cancer" around me. Wanda and I never once spoke it. Nor did any of my other visitors. The nurses were pleasant but noncommittal; the doctors never seemed to have enough time to answer the questions that were tormenting me. "How long do I have to live?" I wanted to ask them. "How long?"

After I'd been in the hospital for about a week, my doctor suggested that the University of Iowa Hospital, in Iowa City, would be better equipped to handle my treatment, and arrangements were made for me to go there in two weeks. I didn't like the sound of his decision. Especially since he only said "treatment." Not once did he say "cure."

At home, I spent most of my time in my den. Alone. I didn't want to be with anyone. My illness had become a barrier between my family and me. I couldn't bring myself to believe what was happening. That I had an incurable disease. That I was dying. I could not imagine the world continuing without me—my children preparing for school, my wife preparing breakfast—and I not there to see it all and to help them along. It became nearly impossible for me to discipline my children when, as children do, they acted up. I was afraid that if I was stern with them, they would remember me only as a harsh father. I couldn't bear the thought of that.

The pressure on Wanda was intolerable too. We had never spoken about death with one another, and now that we were confronted with it, we didn't know what to say. There she was—thirty-one years old, the mother of four children, the breadwinner of the family, the wife of a dying man—with the prospect of widowhood, of having to bring up the family alone. She, too, began to have nightmares that woke her up in tears.

One day, a short while before I was to be admitted to the Iowa City hospital, Wanda left for work as usual and I went back upstairs to lie down in bed. About three hours later, I heard the front door open and someone come running hurriedly up the stairs. It was Wanda. She was sobbing. She mumbled something about breaking down at the factory and the foreman giving her a medical leave of absence.

I grabbed her and hugged her. We both cried.

At University Hospital, I was considered an ambulatory patient. That meant I could move around on my own. When I went from one floor to another for my tests—the X rays, scans, and other more painful procedures I was put through—I was usually given my medical records to take with me. Since the doctors and nurses would not answer the questions I kept asking them about my condition, I took advantage of the opportunity to read the records myself. I would get off the elevator one floor early, and head for the nearest rest room. There I would closet myself in one of the cubicles, and try to decipher the reports. What I read was not encouraging.

"Films of chest show prominence of the left hilar shadow suggestive of primary bronchogenic carcinoma . . ." the record of one chest X ray said. I guessed that meant the cancer had spread to my lungs. Other reports seemed to indicate that it had also invaded the liver and spleen.

The weeks dragged on. One . . . two . . . three . . . four. . . . No one seemed to know how long the tests would take. All I had to look forward to were the weekend furloughs the doctors gave me. Not that my weekends at home were easy. On one of the trips, I had my forty-third birthday, and some friends and relatives stopped by. But the atmosphere was strained. How the word had got around about my illness, I still don't know. But it obviously had. There were long silences, punctuated by the smallest kind of small talk. Suddenly, one of my friends stood up from the couch and ran to the back porch. I followed him, and could see through the kitchen window that he was crying. I went out to join him.

"What's the matter?" I asked.

"I wish it could have been me instead of you," he said, without looking at me.

I didn't know how to answer. I was touched by his emotion, but was still too locked into fear and self-pity to be able to respond. I patted him on the shoulder and went back to the other guests.

Perhaps my worst trip home occurred in the middle of August. I had been in the hospital for more than a month, and no one seemed to be able to tell me anything concrete. Wanda had driven up from Burlington to take me home, and I wanted to get as far away from Iowa City as possible. I must have been a depressing sight. I had lost over 30 pounds, but I still weighed in at a hefty 230; I had been putting on weight ever since I first began to feel sick. My face was drawn and haggard. My shoulders slumped. And, to complete the picture, the doctors had wrapped my feet in plastic bags after the lymphangiogram they had taken that morning, so that I could shower without getting the sutures wet, and I wore a pair of brown house slippers over the bags.

When we reached Burlington, I realized I didn't want to go home.

"I want a drink, Wanda," I said. "Take me to a bar."

"You can't do that," she said. "You're sick. You're weak. The children are waiting. Let's go home."

"I don't care," I insisted. "I want a drink. I want to be where there are people. I want to try to forget what's happening to me."

Wanda tried again to dissuade me. She was close to tears. But I had made up my mind.

"I'm going to have a drink," I said. "If you don't want to come with me, you can go home."

Afraid to leave me alone, Wanda had no choice but to come with me. She helped me from the car, supporting me as we made our way into one of the taverns I had frequented before we were married, when I was in the army and a champion drinker and arm-wrestler. It was crowded and noisy. There was a pool table in the center of the room, surrounded by several hustlers. A jukebox was blaring country and western music in the background. An electric fan was blowing lazily in one corner.

I hadn't had any liquor in several months, and the first shot seemed to calm me. I drank steadily for several hours, Wanda pleading with me all the while to go home with her to the children. But I wouldn't leave. Suddenly a friend entered, a man with whom I used to arm-wrestle before I married.

"Kelly, where the hell have you been?" he asked, walking over to Wanda and me at the bar. "I haven't seen you in years."

"I've been on vacation. Can't you tell?"

He must have noticed how worn I looked. But he said nothing.

"Hey, guys," he called out to the people he had come in with, "come over here. I want you to meet someone I used to know. We used to arm-wrestle. I don't think he ever got beat."

"Well, I still don't think anyone can beat me. Do you want to try?"

Wanda grabbed my arm and pulled at it. "You can't do that," she said to me. "Let's go. Please. Let's go."

I sat there, unmoving.

"He can't arm-wrestle," she said to the others. "He just got out of the hospital. Come on, Kelly. Please." She tugged my arm again.

"The hell with that," I screamed at the top of my voice, pushing her hand off my arm. "I'm going to arm-wrestle."

My friend had joined Wanda in trying to calm me, but he was no more successful than she. I was determined to arm-wrestle someone—and I was determined to win. I was determined to prove I still was a man—even though I had cancer, even though my life was slipping away from me. At the end of the bar was a husky man in work clothes, his face dark with soot. I motioned for him to come over.

"Please," Wanda insisted. "It doesn't matter to me. You don't have to prove anything to me. Please, Kelly, let's go home." She was fighting to keep back the tears.

"What's your name?" I asked the man when he came over.

"Williams. Sam Williams."

"Well, I'm Orville Kelly, and this is my wife, Wanda, and these are my friends. Have you ever arm-wrestled before?"

"Yes. But I won't arm-wrestle with you. You just got out of the hospital. I heard them saying so."

"That's not the reason. You're afraid you'll lose,"

I said. "I may have been in the hospital, but I can still beat you."

He shrugged his shoulders. "OK, if you insist."

He put his beer down and raised a massive arm. We grasped each other's right hands, and someone placed our elbows in line on the bar. His hands were tanned from the sun and his fingers were caked with grease. Next to his, my hands were pale. I could feel his strength as he tightened his grip on my hand. Then someone said "Go," and everyone in the bar turned to look at us.

For the first ten seconds, I was able to hold him to a draw, but then I knew I was beaten. I could feel the pain in my arm as he slowly forced it to the top of the bar and finally slammed my arm down. There was dead silence.

"Let's go," Wanda begged.

I gulped another shot of whiskey. "You're not going to get away that easy," I said to Williams. "Put your other arm on the bar."

He tried to refuse, but I wouldn't let him. By now, I really didn't know what I was doing. I only knew I had once been a champion arm-wrestler. I wanted to prove I still was.

I grabbed Williams' left hand, and we wrestled again. Out of the corner of my eye I could see Wanda. She was shaking.

This time, the match was no contest. I had to bite

my lip to keep from shrieking in pain. It felt as if my arm was being torn off at the shoulder.

When my arm hit the bar this time, I didn't look around to see if anyone was watching. It was no longer possible to pretend that I was the man I used to be. Everyone in the bar knew I wasn't. Wanda knew it. And now I did.

"I buy the drinks," I said, throwing a few bills on the counter.

"Don't feel bad, Kelly," my friend said. "He couldn't have come close to beating you in the old days."

When I tried to stand up to leave, I fell back on the stool. My head was spinning and my stomach was queasy. I hadn't had that much whiskey in years. I had to have Wanda support me on the way out of the tavern.

What had happened to my life? Whose fault was this terrible thing that had happened to me? I had blamed the doctors. I had blamed myself. Now there was only one person left to blame.

"There is no God," I screamed at the top of my voice when we reached the car. "Why me? Why me?" I screamed as my eyes began to water. "There are worse sinners in this world than I am. Why me? God must be dead. Why me?"

I was still sobbing when Wanda finally got me back to the house and into bed.

All the next day, I was haunted by thoughts of suicide. Until then, I had been able to preserve my sense of manhood, and of dignity. But now I had shown the world that I was a dying man—that my life was over. I couldn't think of any reason to prolong the inevitable. I considered driving my car out of control and crashing it. But then I realized I might injure someone else. And besides, it didn't seem a fool-proof plan. I considered poison. But that didn't seem manly. I considered shooting myself. That seemed more appropriate.

Then I suddenly remembered that Christmas was coming in a few more months. I wanted to remember just one more Christmas with my family. I would commit suicide after that.

Hospital life was the same when I returned to Iowa City for more testing. The physicians continued to examine me and continued to evade my questions about my condition. I continued to read my medical records in the rest room, and I knew my situation was not good. Often I wondered if Christmas was worth waiting for.

One morning, about six weeks into my stay at University Hospital, one of my physicians came into the room. I was alone, with my eyes closed. He shut the door, drew a chair up next to my bed, and sat down. He was a slim man, an Oriental with a slight accent. He fixed his eyes on the wall behind my bed and asked, "Has anyone told you the prognosis in your case?"

Finally.

I held my breath. "No," I said.

"We do not feel your cancer can be cured," he said with a slight hesitation. "However, we *do* feel it can be treated."

Suddenly I was overcome by the same feeling I had had in the operating room in Burlington Memorial Hospital. I had known, but I really hadn't known. I had feared being told, and now I was being told. I was going to die.

"How much time do I have?"

"We can't tell you that," he said as he adjusted himself in his chair. "We can only quote you some statistics. And they may not be entirely correct. It all depends on the treatment you receive. And we haven't decided on the most effective treatment for you yet."

"Six months?" I asked.

"We don't know."

"A year?"

Silence.

"Eighteen months?"

"It's hard to say."

"Can't you give me at least some idea?"

"I would say, taking a guess, that you have from six months to three years. But this doesn't mean that you're going to die in six months, or that you'll live as long as three years, or that you'll die when three years are up. You may die sooner or later than these statistics suggest. All we can do is give you something to go by. I'm sorry, but that's the best we can do." He shook his head.

The death sentence was complete.

I managed to thank the doctor for being honest, and he left. I wanted to call Wanda, in Burlington, but I couldn't bring myself to. I wanted to cry, but I couldn't do that either. I thought of Wanda, and of my children. Britty was only four years old; I would never see him grow to be a young man. Why, I asked myself, why? I looked out the window at the healthy people walking around the hospital grounds. Why?

By the middle of September, the doctors had decided that neither surgery nor radiation would be an effective treatment for my illness. They proposed chemotherapy, a treatment that involves taking, both orally and intravenously, a series of poisonous drugs designed to destroy the cancerous cells or at least stop them from multiplying. Chemotherapy may not be a cure; the drugs often destroy healthy cells along with the cancerous ones. Moreover, no one knows for sure how a given patient will react to the treatments. It is at best an effort to buy the patient as much time as possible.

I had confidence in my doctors' medical judgments, and I was prepared to begin the chemotherapy. But a week later, when Wanda came to Iowa City to drive me home, I still hadn't told her about my discussion with the doctor. Nor did I have any plans to tell her. It was a secret that was going to stay inside me.

In some ways, life at home was even harder for me to cope with than life in the hospital had been. Death became an obsession; and in my nightmares the lid of my casket was closed, and I could feel it being lowered slowly into the ground.

Isolation became a way of life for me. I rarely left my bedroom. Indeed, I rarely left my bed. I saw no reason to. I didn't want to read, or write, or watch television. I didn't want to do anything. It had been almost two years since I had worked full-time for a newspaper, and it had been more than two months since I touched the typewriter in my upstairs studio adjoining the bedroom. The walls of that studio were hung with the mementos of my army and newspaper years—the awards from the army, navy and air force for reporting about former GIs; the award from Southern Illinois University for a feature story I'd written; the picture of me with a notebook standing next to Zsa Zsa Gabor when I interviewed her once for a story while I was working near Chicago. But those were only memories—memories that didn't mean much any longer. I wanted to die. I wanted to be rid of life.

Healthy people didn't seem to want to be around me. Some even feared that I would contaminate them. One night, Wanda and I decided to break out of our isolation and went to a party we'd been invited to at the home of a friend. For the first time in months, I was almost enjoying myself—what with the music, the wine, and the conversation. Then I noticed that everyone else in the room had his drink in a glass. Mine was in a paper cup. And there was the time a neighbor came to visit with her two children. As they climbed the stairs to the bedroom where I was lying, I heard the woman ask Wanda, in a whisper: "Are you sure it's all right to bring the children? He's not contagious, is he?"

Ironically, ministers were the least help to me. Several came to visit. Some even told me that my disease was a sign that God had chosen me; that I should wear my cancer as a badge of honor. And the only hope they had to offer was prayer. I needed something more concrete than that. I needed, and did not really have, the will to go on living. I needed to be able to talk honestly and openly to my wife and children. And I could not. I needed to think of myself as a human being. Gravely ill, yes. Under a death sentence. But a human being nevertheless.

The day finally arrived for my first chemotherapy treatment—the day that was to mark a turning point for all of us. At mid-morning, Wanda, Britty, and I left for the all-too-familiar drive to Iowa City. Once at the hospital, I was ushered into a small, white room where a technician took my blood count. Then I was led to a larger room, where I was introduced to a tall, young, studious-looking doctor whose duty it was to initiate me into the mysteries of chemotherapy. A nurse wheeled in a tray loaded with dozens of vials of colorless liquids. My face must have shown my shock: the doctor quickly informed me that only two of the vials were for me. One contained cytoxan, the other vinchristine. Both were to be administered intravenously.

The drugs felt like ice as they ran through my body, and within a few seconds I had a bitter taste in my mouth and a tingling sensation in my nose. And when I tried to sit up after the treatment was completed (the whole thing took no more than seven minutes), I found that I was a little dizzy. But that was all. I wasn't half as sick as I had been when I had tried to stand up three months before in the operating room at the Burlington hospital. I was more frightened than sick.

When I was able to walk out of the room, the nurse handed me a large bottle of pills—two hundred of them—which contained prednisone, the third drug in my treatment. I was to take this orally, forty pills a day for five days. As I headed back to the waiting room, the nurse at the desk told me to return in three and a half weeks for another treatment, and she wrote my name in a book. Three and a half weeks. At least the doctors thought I had three and a half weeks to live. That was the first encouraging sign I had been given in three months.

Despite the treatment, I felt well enough to drive home that afternoon. But the car was silent as the grave. Wanda and I still could not talk to one another about our common problem—my cancer. She was sitting in the front with me and looking fixedly out the window. Britty was taking a nap, stretched out along the back seat.

"You're alive," I suddenly thought to myself. "You're alive. For three months, you've known you have cancer, but you're still alive."

As I steered the car along the rough highway, I began to think of what I had been doing to myself and my family. Without really knowing it, all of us had been celebrating a funeral—mine—and the funeral hadn't even taken place yet. I was still alive. I wasn't dead. *I had some time.* I was forty-three years old, I had a wife who loved me, I had two sons and two daughters.

"What have you got to lose by trying to live with this damned cancer?" a voice in my head asked me. Things couldn't get worse than they were now. The strain under which the family was living was already taking its toll. School had started, and Tammy had brought home failing slips in several of her classes. Mark was sullen much of the time, and Lori was quiet and subdued. No one in my family seemed happy any longer. We had had cancer as a part of our family way of life for more than three months, and no one in our household had mentioned the word once during all that time. What had life been for me since my cancer had first been diagnosed? Tumors . . . bone marrow biopsy . . . lymphangiograms . . . wrestling matches in bars . . . curses . . . tears . . . loneliness . . . nightmares . . . thoughts of suicide . . . paper cups . . . whispers . . . silence. I had been blaming God for all my problems. But now I knew it was up to me to deal with them.

I began to notice how beautiful the autumn day

was. The sun was out. The leaves had just begun to turn; they shone orange, and yellow, and red. Red-winged blackbirds were perched on fence posts. Farmers were out in their fields, preparing for another season. This was life. I was part of it. And I had been depriving myself of it. I stopped the car.

"Wanda," I blurted out. "We've got to talk about it. I have cancer. Cancer! I'll probably die of it. But I'm not dead yet. We have to talk about it."

Wanda turned, stared at me intently, and moved closer to me on the seat. "Are you sure you want to?" she asked.

"Yes, I'm sure. We have to face it together. I know you haven't told me the way you really feel. I don't know how we can help each other if we don't talk about it. I've just been moping around the house and making everyone miserable."

She nodded. "None of us wanted to worry you."

"Let's go home and have a barbecue tonight," I said to her. "We haven't had one in a long time. And we'll have to tell the children. We're just wasting time, and I don't want to go on living like this any longer."

There, I had said it. It was out in the open. Wanda's face seemed to light up; I hadn't seen her like that for more than three months. We kissed as if we really meant it for the first time since I had been told I had cancer. I started the car again, and we drove home.

That evening, I lighted the charcoal in the barbecue grill that had been standing idle for months on our back porch. Wanda bought spareribs at the supermarket, and the whole family had a meal that really tasted like a meal. I even had three beers. (I paid for that indulgence the next morning. My neck felt as if someone had put a clamp on it. I was nauseated, my legs hurt, and I felt very weak. Which was enough to persuade me never again to drink beer immediately after a treatment.)

Around nine o'clock, Wanda took Britty upstairs to bed, and I took Tammy, Mark, and Lori out to the back porch. Our porch is small, with room only for a few chairs and a couch. But the view is open all the way down to the Mississippi River. The stars were out that night, and the full moon threw its sparkles on the surface of the water. I sat down on the couch, the three children around me.

"I think it's time you knew what's wrong with me," I started. "This may take a while for me to explain, but you all should know." I hesitated for a moment—it was not going to be easy to tell them this. Then I looked at the moon, took a deep breath, and continued. "The doctors have told me that I have cancer. Cancer is a disease that destroys tissues inside your body. That's why I've been sick so much. The doctors say that in all probability unless something else happens first, I will die of cancer."

Tammy and Lori began to cry. Mark sat motionless.

"But I'm not dead yet. I'm going to stay alive as long as I possibly can. Your mother and I went to Iowa City today so I could start treatments. We'll have to make the best of it. I'll tell you when things are good and when they're bad, but I want you three to help me live with this cancer. There will be bad days for us, but we can have good days, too. We don't have to like death, but we don't have to be terrified by it, either."

Finally, it was out in the open. Now, everyone knew except Britty; Wanda and I both felt he was too young to understand. I hugged each child. Tammy and Lori still had tears in their eyes. Mark was still silent. But now he accepted the fact that I had cancer. I had told him. He believed me. He no longer felt his mother had lied to him that day in June at the hospital.

When I went upstairs to our bedroom, I had one more thing to do before going to bed. I took a piece of paper from the desk in my studio, and wrote the word DEATH on it. This was my death that I was spelling out. I had to face it, just as my family did. I looked at that piece of paper for about five minutes —looked and looked and looked. Then I slowly put it back in the desk drawer and got ready for bed. Wanda had been sleeping in the den ever since she had begun to have nightmares. But that night, for the first time in a long time, we slept in the same bed together.

Soon after the first chemotherapy treatment, I asked Wanda to help me clean up the studio. The desk, the bookcases, and the typewriter were deep in dust, but we finally managed to make the room spotless. I hadn't written anything for a long while—not since a day when, on the bus to Burlington, on the way home for a weekend away from the hospital, I had composed a poem for Wanda:

Spring, and the land lies fresh-green
Beneath a yellow sun.
We walked the land together, you and I
And never knew what future days would bring.
Will you often think of me,
When flowers burst forth each year?
When the earth begins to grow again?
Some say death is so final.

But my love for you can never die.
Just as the sun once warmed our hearts,
Let this love touch you some night,
When I am gone,
And loneliness comes—
Before the dawn begins to scatter
Your dreams away.

Summer, and I never knew a bird
Could sing so sweet and clear,
Until they told me I must leave you
For a while.
I never knew the sky could be so deep a blue,
Until I knew I could not grow old with you.
But better to be loved by you,
Than to have lived a million summers,
And never known your love.
Together, let us, you and I
Remember the days and nights,
For eternity.

Fall, and the earth begins to die,
And leaves turn golden-brown upon the trees.
Remember me, too, in autumn, for I will walk with
 you,
As of old, along a city sidewalk at evening-time,
Though I cannot hold you by the hand.

Winter, and perhaps someday there may be
Another fireplace, another room,
With crackling fire and fragrant smoke,
And turning, suddenly we will be together,
And I will hear your laughter and touch your face,
And hold you close to me again.
But, until then, if loneliness should seek you out,
Some winter night, when snow is falling down,
Remember, though death has come to me,
Love will never go away!

Now I began to write again. One of my first pieces was about a Christmas I remembered. I was seven years old, it was during the Great Depression, and we were living on a rundown farm. In times as hard as those, I didn't think I would get any presents. A blizzard had developed on Christmas Eve, and I had snuggled into a featherbed to keep warm, praying that I would get just a little something for Christmas. When I woke the next morning and went downstairs, I found a decorated Christmas tree in the front room, and underneath it, a pair of lace-up boots, a red fire engine, and a sack of candy.

"I have seen many other snowfalls," I wrote, "but for some reason I always remember that night when the blizzard came on Christmas Eve. Whenever I see the snow coming down and hear the wind begin to howl, I remember a dream that came true."

I submitted the story to the local Burlington newspaper—the *Hawk-Eye*—for a winter writing contest and received a first prize for it. That was my first Christmas present of the year. And others came, too. I hadn't expected much for the Kellys that Christmas. Wanda and I had only a little money, although we had been able to make ends meet with the Social Security disability payments and Veterans Administration checks we had been receiving. But Christmas 1973 turned out to be one of the warmest our family ever had, thanks to the generosity of a few friends, particularly those at the factory where Wanda had worked. We received cash, hams, turkeys, and countless boxes of candy. Wanda bought a few presents for the children. Most important, the entire family was together.

The day after Christmas, I decided it was time for me to write about the struggles of a cancer patient. Before I knew that I had cancer, I had thought of it as similar to leprosy—a disease that rotted people slowly—and visibly—away. Life with cancer didn't have to be that way, and I wanted people to know this. Of course, I didn't have all the answers, but I wanted to show that cancer could be approached with openness, and that dying people *did* have something to live for. Although I had read about all the money being spent on cancer research, I had heard very little about the emotional rehabilitation of cancer patients and their families. The void was obvious. No matter how the problem of cancer is handled in a family, all the members of the family are bound to be affected in some way.

I spent two days writing and editing the piece. "Once," I wrote in it, "I asked how there could be a God who would let so many terrible things happen. Now I ask myself how I can doubt the existence of God . . . when I hear a child's laughter on a summer evening, or see around me the miracle of life itself. When I hold my hand to my chest and feel the beat of my heart and realize this is life and I am part of it, I know there has to be a God. When I think to myself how lucky I was to have such an understanding person as my wife, Wanda, I know good things happen. When someone does a kind thing for me, I know this is all part of this miracle of living.

"On Christmas a Burlington woman called to tell me her husband had been told recently he had lung cancer. She wanted to know if I would come to their house and talk to him. He felt he would like to just sit down and talk to someone with the same problems he had.

"The thought came to me that there should be some kind of organization of people with incurable diseases. These people could help each other, and I am going to work on this. . . ."

I sent the story to the *Hawk-Eye,* and the editors

decided to use it in the Sunday, January 6, edition. The story was carried on page 2, along with a picture of me looking out from our back porch and another picture of me taking my pills. The day the story appeared, I received several telephone calls from other cancer patients, telling me how strongly they supported my idea of forming an organization. So I arranged for a gathering at the local Elks Club on January 25. With the help of a little publicity from the local newspaper, eighteen cancer patients and members of their families, including Wanda and me, met that night in the upstairs meeting room.

One of the first things I told the group was that I didn't think we were there to cry on one another's shoulders. We weren't there to find out who was the most seriously ill. We were there to share our mutual problems and to try to work them out so that we could live as close to normal lives as possible. We went around the table introducing ourselves and telling our stories as a way to break the ice. After some discussion, we decided we should try to get together once a month to talk with one another and to listen to speakers who could help us face our illnesses.

Several days before the meeting, it had occurred to me that if we were going to start a group, we ought to have a name. I had three suggestions: Live

Each Day Fully; Live For Today; or Make Today Count.

When I put the suggestions to a vote, the other seventeen hands were raised in support of my choice.

The vote was for *Make Today Count.*

TWO

I still chuckle when I think of the look of surprised disbelief that suffused the face of the young reporter who came to interview me for one of the Iowa newspapers shortly after Make Today Count was first organized.

"Are you sure *you're* Orville Kelly?" his look said. "Are you sure you're a dying man?"

I can understand his bafflement. I don't look sick; I look healthy. I'm tall—six feet—and stand quite straight and erect: an inheritance from my twelve years of army life. And the excess weight I carry—much of it a side effect of my chemotherapy treatments—is pretty well distributed. I don't appear flabby. There's color in my face; my hair is still black. Most of all, I don't *want* to look sick. I want to look like what I am: an ordinary, forty-four-year-old Iowan with a wife and four children—a man with roots and with ties of love to other people. A man whose life has meaning for him.

That meaning took me a long time to find. I'm sure one of the reasons I felt so despairing—even suicidal—when my cancer was first diagnosed was that, until I became a husband and father, my life had no real sense of direction. I had no real sense of belonging—anywhere, or to anyone. I'd finally found a direction, and people I belonged to. It seemed especially cruel that I was going to have to lose what it had taken me so long to find.

I started out by not belonging. My mother was only sixteen, and unmarried, when she gave birth to me on August 2, 1930, in the back room of her parents' white frame house in the small, sleepy town of Columbus Junction, in eastern Iowa. She was still in high school, and too young to assume the responsibility of bringing up a child; she and my grandparents agreed that as soon as she graduated, she would leave home, and I would remain in their care. My grandparents were Nathan and Maude Thompson, and I was given their last name: I was christened Orville Eugene Thompson. My grandfather was a short, stocky man in his late forties when I was born; my grandmother, a few years younger, was quiet and unassuming—a deeply religious woman whose greatest comfort was the Bible she seemed always to carry with her. Neither of them had any more than a grade school education, but they were hard-working people. Until the Great Depression hit the Midwest full-force, they had always been able to make a decent living from the small restaurant they owned. But the Depression forced them out of business, and forced my grandfather to become a hired farmhand, moving his family throughout southeastern Iowa and western Illinois in search of work.

Almost from the beginning, I knew I was different from other children. They called the adults in their lives "momma" and "poppa"; I called my grown-ups "grandma" and "grandpa." Other children's parents were younger, and more lively; other children had sisters and brothers—youngsters their own age to play with. By the time I was eight, I had discovered what it was that made me different. Through conversations I overheard when my grandparents thought I was safely out of earshot, I learned that one of the "aunts" who occasionally visited us was not, in fact, my aunt. She was my mother. But neither she nor my grandparents ever said anything to me about it, and sensing that to mention this whole matter was to tread on dangerous territory, I said not a word to them. I was bewildered and hurt at what I could only experience as my mother's abandonment of me. I envied other children, whose mothers acknowledged and loved them. But I kept my feelings bottled up inside, and eventually I was even able to persuade myself that I didn't care.

When I think back over my childhood, the things that stand out with most clarity are that sense of loneliness and differentness from other children and the sense of rootlessness I always had. Our family seemed always to be on the move, in search of farm work for my grandfather. We were never in one place even as long as a year; just as I'd gotten settled in and gotten used to things, it would be time to pack up and move on to another farm. We'd rise at sunrise and, after a meager breakfast of hotcakes with bacon-grease gravy, my grandparents would pack our belongings and hitch the team of horses onto the small, open wagon for the journey. Grandpa and grandma would sit on the front seat, and I would be perched on the back—together with Tom, the cat; two dogs, Pooch and Freddy, and all the family furniture. As we bumped along, I'd gaze out at the fields of corn and soybean and at the cattle grazing in the pastures that lined the bumpy, dirt back roads. And I'd wonder to myself what our next home would be like.

The home we found in Farmington, Iowa, is the one I remember with most affection, and the months we lived there were the happiest of my childhood. Until then, the only concept I had of a world outside the rural Midwest was formed from the programs we used to listen to on our old, battery-powered Atwater Kent radio. But while we lived in Farmington—I was nine at the time—I saw my first movie. It was—I still remember it vividly—*Buck Benny Rides Again*, and it starred that great comedian Jack Benny. Equally vivid in my memory is my first sight of the Farmington house—a two-story, unpainted wooden structure burned a dirty grayish-brown by the rays of the sun. As we approached it, I could see the shutters hanging loose from the windows, and the screen door, which had fallen from its hinges, lying crazily across the front porch. In the back, I could see the small garden patch, overgrown with morning glories; I could see the outhouse and the chicken coop. The building wasn't particularly prepossessing inside, either. There was no electricity, only some kerosene lamps mounted on the walls. The front room had nothing in it but a rickety table and some equally rickety chairs. And my room, upstairs, contained nothing but a mattress lying on the floor. There wasn't even a dresser. Not that I needed one. My entire wardrobe consisted of a pair of bib overalls and a blue denim shirt.

The first night we moved in, after my grandparents had gone to bed, and when they thought I was sleeping, I took one of the kerosene lamps and, walking on tiptoe so as to make no noise, climbed the short ladder that led to the attic, pushed up the floor door, and walked into a world the existence of which I'd never even dreamed. Stacked all over the attic floor were books, newspapers, magazines, and catalogues—a virtual sea of them. The lamplight caught the title of one book: *The Swiss Family Robinson.* I picked it up and, clutching it to me, returned to my room. I lay down on my mattress, set the kerosene lamp beside me, and started to read. Many of the words had no meaning for me, but the pictures seemed literally to jump off the page. Tropical jungles; tree houses; a happy-looking family: it was a world I could not even have imagined. I finally fell asleep, my head resting on the open book; when I woke the next morning, I continued reading until I had to make an appearance downstairs. On my trip to the attic the next night, I found a dog-eared dictionary. Now I could discover the meanings of the words I didn't understand, and reading became an even more exciting adventure.

When I had finished *The Swiss Family Robinson,* I devoured all the other books and magazines I found upstairs: the Bobbsey Twins series; the

Rover Boys adventure stories; the Campfire Girls books; the copies of the *Saturday Evening Post* and *Colliers*. But my favorite of all was the dime-novel series about the adventures of cowboy Wayne Morgan and his horse, Midnight. All that summer, my favorite game was pretending I was Wayne Morgan, and pretending that my grandfather's Jersey cow was really a horse named Midnight.

September, and school, came all too soon that year. I'd rather have stayed home, reading and pretending to be Wayne Morgan. School was in a white one-room building that stood among the trees in the corner of a neighboring pasture about a mile from our house, at the end of a back road that led through fields of wild flowers. The school's total enrollment was nine children; I, in lonely splendor, made up the entire fourth grade. I made no friends among the children who attended school with me. I had already developed the habit of shyness; I was ashamed to bring anyone home with me lest they discover I had no "real" parents. Besides—or so I convinced myself—it was more fun to read my newly discovered books than to play with other youngsters.

But the house with the wonderland attic, like all the other houses I'd lived in, was home for only a year. A new season meant more traveling for grandpa to find work; more strangers; more one-room country schoolhouses and more old farm-houses with cracks so large that in winter the snow could always find a home in the living room.

When I was twelve, we moved to Burlington, where my grandfather found a job at the Army Ordnance plant, operating at full capacity to serve the demands of the Second World War. We moved into an apartment near the plant and, for the first time in my life, I discovered what indoor plumbing was. For the first time, too, I went to a school with more than one room, and I went to the same school for more than a year. For a while, it seemed that things were getting better. We'd settled down in one place; there was more financial security than I could ever remember. But then the relationship between my grandparents began to deteriorate. They quarreled, ever more frequently and ever more angrily. One day, when I'd just turned fifteen, my grandfather ran off with a woman he'd met at the plant.

That brought another change to my life. My grandmother, now in her fifties, had to go to work. And although she was able to earn enough to support herself, she didn't feel able, either financially or emotionally, to continue taking care of me. So I was shipped off to the small town of Wapello, Iowa, about thirty miles from Burlington, where my mother's sister Mae lived with her husband, Willie, and their son, Jimmy, who was about ten years younger than I.

While my grandparents and I were living in Burlington, we paid several visits to Mae, Willie, and Jimmy. The visits were warm and friendly, and all of us got along well. But once I became a permanent resident of Willie and Mae's home, everything changed. And not for the better. Mae tried to be a mother to me, but Willie made no effort at all to be a father. I was, in his view, an outsider, and he never accepted me. What's more, he made it obvious—so obvious that, after I'd been in Wapello only a few weeks, I ran away to Burlington to be with my grandmother. But grandma had meant it when she said she could no longer take care of me. She telephoned Aunt Mae, and Willie drove to Burlington to take me back to Wapello. I still remember the terrible, icy silence of that ride. Willie didn't say a single word to me during the entire trip.

The years with Mae and Willie were unhappy ones for me, and I retreated even further into myself and into the books, borrowed from the school library, that I read, in my attic bedroom, until long after I was supposed to have been asleep. My favorite was James Michener's *Tales of the South Pacific;* like *The Swiss Family Robinson,* it took me out of my everyday world into an exotic island paradise.

As soon as I'd come to Wapello, Mae wanted to adopt me—to make me, officially, her child. But Willie resisted the idea until I'd been with them for nearly a year. When I was sixteen, a junior in the Wapello High School, I became, officially, their son. My name was changed from Orville Eugene Thompson to Orville Eugene Kelly. The change was, I'm sure, much easier for my classmates to adjust to than it was for me.

I didn't dislike school, but I didn't like it much either, and my grades reflected my lack of interest: I was only an average student. Except in speech and English. I was captain of the school speech team, and the English composition class awakened my desire to write. One of my poems even made the Yearbook, the year I was graduated:

Did you ever sit on your porch at night,
When the moon was out and the stars were bright,
And listen to the croaking of the frogs in the pond,
And look into the darkness and wonder what's
beyond?

The world beyond was the world I wanted to enter. The adventures I'd read about in the books I devoured had shown me that life had more to offer than moving from farm to farm and from family to family in the secluded sections of rural Iowa. When I was in my last year at high school, an army recruiter had come to talk to the boys in my class; from what he told us, the army sounded like the great escape. I was only seventeen, and a skinny 140 pounds, but the recruiter seemed to think I'd do. And Willie was only too happy to sign the release papers which, because I was not yet eighteen, the army required. I graduated from high school at the end of June, 1948, and the next week reported to Rock Island, Illinois, for my physical examination.

Mae cried when I left Wapello. But although I was fond of her, and it hurt me to see her unhappy, I was glad to get away from Willie, from Iowa, and from my lonely past.

For the next twelve years, the army was my home and my way of life—a way of life as migratory as my childhood had been. At first, it was full of adventure and glamour. But later I discovered that the army had rough edges; that it was not the home I was looking for.

I took my basic training at Fort Knox, Kentucky, and when I finished it, I took additional courses in typing and stenography, and was promoted to buck sergeant. That office training was my ticket to faraway places. In April of 1949 I was sent to Japan as part of the Allied occupation of the country under the direction of General Douglas MacArthur, and was assigned to the Chief of Staff section, Eighth Army, in Yokohama.

Yokohama is one of Japan's larger cities. By the time I arrived there, it was bustling with postwar activities, many of them designed to serve the needs and wants of the occupying force. The streets were crowded with small shops and marketplaces, with dimly lit *sake* houses and with cabarets. There were funny little streetcars running up and down the main streets; taxis that burned charcoal; and rickshaws pulled by men with haggard faces, wearing coolie hats. The downtown area was ringed with rolling hills, covered with countless matchbox houses. It was as exotic as any Iowa farmboy could have wished.

My work at Headquarters kept me busy during the day, but my nights were my own; and although curfew for all GIs was midnight, none of the brass seemed really to care whether curfew was observed. As long as we were not out on the streets after the witching hour, everything was all right.

It didn't take me and my friends long to discover the Japanese cabarets. They became our regular evening hangouts, and we would stay for hours, drinking *sake* or beer and dancing with the cabaret girls. It was in the Cherry Blooming Cabaret that, about two months after I arrived in Yokohama, I met Toshyko, a short, slender girl with long black hair that hung down to her waist, and brown oval eyes that sparkled in even the faintest lights. Toshyko was only sixteen, but she seemed much older: strong, yet gentle; cautious, yet susceptible; harsh, yet tender; Toshyko was like no other girl I had ever known before. Never before, after all, had I known a girl who had grown up with war's destruction, and who lived in a country occupied by the troops of a victorious enemy force. Not that I realized, at the time, how difficult and traumatizing Toshyko's life must have been—more difficult and traumatizing even than mine. In retrospect, I think that was part of what attracted us to one another. Both of us had known a good deal of unhappiness. But at the time, all I knew was that Toshyko was very pretty and very outgoing, and that she summed up, for me, all the romance and glamour of the mysterious Orient.

The first evening we met, I walked her home after the cabaret closed. She knew very little English and I knew very little Japanese, but we seemed to be able to communicate nevertheless. When we arrived at the small house, in a decaying section of town, in which she lived with her parents, she invited me to come in. It was my first visit to a Japanese home, with its walls made of sliding paper panels, its sparse furnishings, its requirement that everyone take off his shoes inside the house. Through a window, I could see a small flower garden, a fish pond, and a tall wooden fence. Toshyko's parents were sitting at a small, round table; they bowed at me, I bowed at them; we smiled. Mama-san, a slender, pleasant woman, was probably in her thirties. But she looked more like forty-five. Papa-san, a short, stocky man in his forties with a broad smile and gray-black hair cut so short that you could see his scalp shining through, was a former member of the Japanese cavalry who liked to drink and to tell stories of the cruelty of the American army. He poured me a small glass of *sake*, and the two of us sat on the floor and traded drinks while Toshyko and mama-san watched. The more papa-san drank, the more excited he became, until finally he reached for the sword that was hanging on the wall behind him.

"GIs no good . . . gangsters!" he yelled in broken English, waving the sword wildly at me.

I moved back from the table and looked over to Toshyko and mama-san, hoping they would give me some clue as to what to do. But they said nothing.

"How about going out and getting some more

sake?" I said to Toshyko, nervously taking a few yen from my pocket.

I had apparently done the right thing. Papa-san looked at me and smiled. "You number one. Good GI," he said, laying the sword on the floor next to him.

We resumed our drinking until papa-san finally grew tired and left the room with mama-san to retire for the night. When they were gone, Toshyko invited me to stay.

I was happier in Japan than I had ever been before. During the day, I worked in the Chief of Staff's office, helping with the paper work that kept the Occupation going. During the evenings, I was with Toshyko. No one before had ever taken so much interest in me; no one before had ever showed me so much love and care. We were young and we were in love, and we spent many nights together at her parents' home. I was earning $100 a month, and had free room and board at the barracks, so I had money to give Toshyko for living expenses when, at my suggestion, she quit her job at the cabaret. I ate at her house almost every evening; when I arrived, she would be waiting for me with a bottle of Nippon beer and a warm *sukiyaki* dinner. During the evenings, we would sit listening to the strains of "China Nights" on a small, hand-wound phonograph, to the sounds of children playing in the streets, and to the mournful calls of the blind masseur who walked the narrow alley in front of the house in search of customers. Late at night, the sounds of foghorns and of the waves breaking in the harbor would drift into Toshyko's bedroom, quietly lulling us to sleep.

Although I had picked up a fair amount of Japanese, we usually conversed in English, and one of my great pleasures was reading poetry to her. She always listened attentively, but she didn't always understand. Once she spent several days translating a poem she had written about a Japanese girl and an American soldier who fell in love but were forced to part, and who both committed suicide so they could spend eternity together. Later, after Toshyko and I parted, I often thought of that poem.

On weekends, we used to go to the enlisted men's club, in downtown Yokohama, Toshyko wearing a red silk kimono with black dragons embroidered on it, that I had bought for her. From the garden rooftop of the club, we could see the vast night skies and the bustling night life of the city.

The months passed quickly. My life was filled with my work, with Toshyko, and with the roistering, drinking, and gaiety that are traditional for a peacetime GI. But while I was enjoying myself, the political climate in the Far East was changing. By 1949, the Chinese Communist Revolution had succeeded, and intelligence reports showed that an explosive situation was brewing between North and South Korea. On June 25, 1950, the North Koreans attacked South Korea, and the U.S. Army was mobilized to go to South Korea's aid. My unit was among those sent to Korea. When I left Toshyko, we clung together and promised one another we'd write.

If peacetime Japan had been an idyll for me, wartime Korea was a nightmare. In the villages, little children with stomachs bloated from malnutrition lay asleep in the streets, flies swarming around their mouths and eyes. The stench of sour cabbage was always in the air. I was assigned to the office of the Commanding General, Lieutenant General Walton H. Walker. I worked in the war room, keeping the battle maps up to date and discovering daily just how unprepared our troops were and how ill equipped, with their World War II weapons, to meet the enemy. I never had to use a weapon in combat, but several of my friends were transferred to the front lines; and some were wounded, captured, or killed.

For the first two months I was in Korea, Toshyko

and I continued to write one another—Toshyko sometimes as often as three times a week, in a funny, phonetic English that was full of expressions of love. I wrote less often than she did, but I continued to send her money so that she wouldn't have to work in the cabaret. But then Toshyko's letters began to come less frequently, and began to lose their warmth. I was concerned. I had never seriously thought about marrying Toshyko—I was, after all, only nineteen and not yet ready to settle down—but she meant a lot to me, and I expected our relationship to continue.

In the middle of September, I received orders to return to the States for another assignment. I was delighted. I had seen enough of Korea and of war to last me a lifetime. And I would have a two-day stopover in Japan. That would give me time to see Toshyko again.

As soon as I arrived in Yokohama, I rushed to her home. Papa-san and mama-san were sitting on the floor around the table, just as they had been the first time Toshyko brought me there. But something was different. They looked at me when I came in, but this time they did not bow.

"Where's Toshyko?" I asked, looking around the room.

No answer.

"Where's Toshyko?" I asked again, thinking perhaps they did not understand.

Still no answer.

"Where's Toshyko?" I was talking loudly now.

Papa-san finally raised his head and spoke. "She no here," he said.

"Well, where did she go?"

Again silence.

"Where did she go, dammit!"

"With soldier."

"What kind of soldier?"

"GI."

I didn't like the idea that Toshyko was seeing other men, but I was prepared to forget about it.

"OK, she's out with another soldier. When will they be back?"

Silence.

"When will they be back?" By now I was shouting.

"They no say." Papa-san paused. After a moment, he continued. "They marry."

"Marry?" I wanted to lean against something solid, but the paper walls would not support my weight. I sat down heavily on the floor. "They couldn't have. What do you mean, married? When?"

"Week, week and a half ago."

"This has got to be a joke. I'm talking about Toshyko. Where can I find her?"

"Don't know." Papa-san shrugged his shoulders. "Soldier leave; she leave with him."

I rushed to Toshyko's bedroom. It was bare. I felt weak and dizzy. Papa-san and mama-san said nothing as I walked back into the main room.

"Why?" I asked.

No response. I put on my shoes and knocked the door open as I walked out. First my mother, then my grandmother. And now Toshyko. That night I got drunker than I'd ever been before in my life.

For the next seven years, I was on duty with the army in the United States, in France, and in cold-war Germany. I wanted to stay as far away from Iowa as I could. It held no happy memories for me. In the summer of 1952 I had learned—too late to attend the funeral—of the death of Mae Kelly, my adoptive mother, and the only person in the world whom I thought of as family after my grandmother died.

Now I was a professional soldier. Weight lifting had filled out my once-skinny frame and, with my newfound strength, I had become a champion arm-wrestler. By the time I was twenty-three, and stationed in Germany, I had been promoted to sergeant-major—which made me the youngest U.S. sergeant-major in that country.

One night, at the enlisted men's club, I ran into a

GI with whom I'd served in Yokohama and who had remained there after I was sent to Korea. Like me, he'd had a Japanese girl friend. The minute I saw him, I was reminded of Toshyko—the girl who had deserted me, the girl who had made me leery of ever falling in love again. But I decided to say nothing. So we simply chatted and drank beer for an hour or more.

Finally I decided to speak up. After all, what was wrong with telling an old buddy that a girl had done you dirt?

"Say," I said, trying to sound casual, "do you remember that girl I was going with? Toshyko? The girl from the Cherry Blooming Cabaret? Did you ever hear how she ran out on me?"

My friend looked at me strangely. "Didn't you know?" he asked.

"Know what?" I asked.

My friend hesitated for a moment. "I don't know how to tell you this. But since you asked . . ." He swallowed, and then spoke. "She's dead," he said, expressionlessly.

All the anger and resentment I'd felt against Toshyko suddenly drained from me. I finally managed to speak.

"What happened?"

"Well, the way I heard it from my girl friend, she killed herself. Cut her wrists and drank some poison. She doesn't seem to have wanted to take any chances that she'd fail."

I turned my head away and closed my eyes, trying to keep the tears from welling over. It had been almost three years since I'd last seen Toshyko—since I'd gone to her home and found she'd run off with another soldier.

"I'm sorry, Kelly. I thought you'd heard about it. I guess it must have happened just after you went stateside."

I looked into my beer mug in silence. And I thought of the poem Toshyko had written—the poem about the American GI and the Japanese girl who had committed suicide together rather than part. Then I heard my friend's voice.

"What do you say we call it a night, Kelly?"

I nodded. I wanted to be alone. When I returned to the barracks, I went straight to my footlocker and pulled out the pictures I had carried with me ever since I had left Japan. They showed a U.S. soldier and a Japanese girl dressed in a red silk kimono with black dragons, sitting in a rickshaw smiling, with arms around one another.

When, in the spring of 1957, I learned that assignments were available in the South Pacific, I rushed to sign up. I was twenty-seven years old and completing my tenth year in the army. It was about time for me to get a look at that tropical world on which the Swiss Family Robinson had been shipwrecked, that South Pacific paradise James Michener had written about in *Tales of the South Pacific.* I'd wanted to find out about them ever since I was a kid.

I was assigned to Japtan, a small island in the Marshall Islands chain, which was part of the Eniwetok Atoll—the scene, I remembered, of fierce fighting between the United States and Japan during the Second World War.

At first, Japtan appeared to be a true paradise. It was a tiny island, only two miles long and less than a mile wide. On the lagoon side, the white sands of the beach extended into blue-green waters, so clear that you could see the glorious-hued tropical fish swimming in their depths. There were coconut trees everywhere, and large green lizards and coconut crabs scuttled along the beach. By day, the sun's rays battered the island, but the nights brought cool ocean breezes and the sound of the waves gently lapping the shore. It seemed a perfect place to think, to take stock of things, to find peace and tranquility.

I was made commander of the island, which was known as Site David, and of the thirty men who, with me, would be responsible—so we were told—

for receiving and relaying top-secret messages. What neither I nor any of my men knew, but soon would discover, was that the Eniwetok Atoll, together with the nearby Bikini Islands, was to be the site for the testing of thermonuclear bombs by the United States. During my thirteen months on the island, I witnessed more than three dozen of these blasts from only a short distance away from ground zero. Each blast was a glimpse of hell.

From the beginning, morale on the island was poor. The bomb blasts terrified all of us. When I was in Yokohama, I had heard about the bombs that devastated Hiroshima and Nagasaki; these bombs were capable of doing even more damage than that. And we had no way of knowing whether they would ever be used. If they *were* used, it could mean the end of the world.

To make things worse, there was nothing on the island to take our minds off the horror of the bomb blasts. There were no women, no movies, no entertainment—there wasn't much else to do but drink and play cards. Personality conflicts arose among the men, and there was drunkenness and fighting. A few of the men became involved in homosexual activities. Since there were no military police to help me maintain discipline, I had to take stern measures, and I became the target of all the men's rage at an assignment they all hated. I could feel the resentment simmering inside them. I could even see it in the way they looked at me. I knew I was losing control of the situation, but I wasn't sure what to do. I was also becoming concerned about possible radiation exposure from the nuclear fall-out. Even though I had been assured that we were in no danger, it had rained several times after blasts, and the Geiger counter seemed to jump madly when pointed at several of the ponds on the island.

I'd been on Japtan no more than a few months when it began to get to me. I was nervous; I had frequent nightmares; I was drinking heavily and adding weight to my once-firm physique. I told the doctor that my nerves were frayed, but he only pre-scribed the usual phenobarbital. I requested a trans-fer to another island, but the request was denied.

The twentieth bomb detonation and its aftermath were the worst of them all. We had been notified that the blast would occur at 6:00 in the morning and, according to regulations, we would all have to be in uniform and on the beach at 5:45 to wit-ness it. At 5:00, I staggered out of bed to get dressed and call roll. The sun was just beginning to rise above the ocean as I walked out of my room and onto the white sands of the beach on the way to the men's barracks. The ocean was quiet, the leaves on the coconut trees were motionless; not a breeze stirred the air. Even the men were silent as they rose, dressed hastily, and came running out of their quarters, to line up in two rows. They were wearing special clothing, dark glasses, and helmets that held film badges to register the radiation. I called the roll, ordered the men to face eastward, and then allowed them to stand at ease. It was 5:55 A.M. The seconds ticked by slowly as the men stood there, their legs slightly apart and their hands behind their backs. They were, in military parlance, "at ease." But "at ease" was not the way to describe either them or me.

Over a receiver from headquarters came the countdown. Ten . . . nine . . . eight . . . seven . . . six . . . five . . . four . . . three . . . two . . . one. The peace was destroyed. Several miles away, there was a brilliant flash of yellow fire followed by a wave of heat and a tremendous crackling roar. Finally, a pinkish-red mushroom cloud developed, which did not dissipate for more than two hours and which blocked out the sun's rays until the middle of the afternoon.

That night, as always after a bomb blast, the men held a party in the recreation hall. By the time I got there, they already had an hour's head start on me. They had been drinking heavily, and several of them were already pretty far gone. One of the men had brought in a small record player, and the hall was filled with the sound of dance music. Several of the men were dancing with one another in the middle of the floor. I walked to a corner of the room and sat down alone with a bottle of whiskey. Nearby was a huddle of soldiers, drinking and talking and, finally, arguing—more and more loudly and more and more angrily, until two of them began to fight.

"All right, break it up," I said, as I grabbed one of them by the arm. "That's enough."

The soldier jerked his arm away and snatched up a beer bottle.

"Get your hands off me, SIR," he bellowed drunkenly. "I've had it up to here with your damn orders. This ain't boot camp. I don't have to take those kind of orders from you."

He broke the beer bottle on the edge of a nearby table and poked its menacing, sharp edges in my direction.

"Look at this, SIR. It's a broken bottle, and it's meant for you. When you fall asleep tonight, you're going to find it in your gut."

His voice was so loud and threatening that it carried all through the room. Someone turned off the phonograph and the men stopped dancing. Everyone was silent, looking at the soldier and me. There was nothing I could do—no way for me to enforce discipline against the drunken GI. All I could do was retrieve my bottle of whiskey and walk slowly out of the room.

I kept the light on all that night, and didn't sleep at all.

Experts have never been able to agree as to the amount of exposure to radiation necessary to cause cancer in humans. One of my medical records showed that gamma radiation at a level of 3.15 rep had been recorded on my film badge. During my physical examination after I left Japtan, I asked the doctor what that figure meant, but he never gave me any explanation. Anyway, at that point I was more concerned about my mental health than about my physical condition. Thirteen months on a lonely island, watching bomb blasts and trying to deal with unruly soldiers, had taken their toll of me. I wanted psychiatric help, and I asked for it repeatedly. But instead the army gave me a certificate of achievement for my activities on Japtan.

When I returned to the States in April of 1959, I was twenty-eight years old and had spent eleven years of my life in the army—eleven years that I now considered a total, utter waste. It was—until I discovered I had cancer—the lowest point in my life.

I had a forty-five day leave coming, and something urged me back to Iowa—to Burlington, where I had lived for a few years with my grandparents. Once there, I gravitated straight to the skid-row bars, where I spent all my time doing what I'd done so much of on Japtan—drinking. My ambition and my desire for adventure had vanished, and I was no longer in charge of my emotions. I even began to doubt my sanity. I had no sense of purpose. I had no family, no one I could turn to. All I had were barroom acquaintances—other lost souls with whom to drink.

Finally, I got myself into serious trouble—for a drunken escapade I don't remember clearly to this day. I wound up spending four months in the Des Moines County jail, charged with a misdemeanor stemming from that escapade.

Jail was no paradise, but it wasn't too bad. And the months I spent there gave me time to try to put my life back into perspective. Although the nightmare of Japtan had destroyed my enthusiasm for the army, it was the only home I'd had throughout my adult life. And now I was in trouble with it. I'd been AWOL for nearly four months, and was facing charges of desertion. But when my jail sentence was up, and I was sent to Fort Monmouth, the court-martial board treated me with leniency. Ever since my enlistment, I'd had an excellent record, and my defense counsel was persuasive. Most of my stripes were taken away from me and I was demoted to corporal even before the court-martial, but the outcome of my trial was a suspended sentence and a $50 fine. So I had another chance to win a place in my home.

In the past, I'd always won that place by searching for adventure in a foreign country, so that seemed the thing to do now. Except that I discovered the only overseas duty available was in Korea. I'd been there once before, during the war, and my memories of the country were not fond. But now I felt that I was in control of my life and could handle any problems that might arise. And I wanted to regain the stripes I'd lost. Korea seemed my best chance. My tour of duty was to start in November, after a three-week furlough. I decided to return once more to Burlington, to spend my furlough there.

The first evening of my furlough, I stopped in at Tiny's Cafe, in downtown Burlington, for dinner. It was an unpretentious-looking place, but it seemed clean and quiet; as I looked in through the window, there wasn't a customer to be seen. I was feeling lonely and discouraged—ashamed that I'd lost my stripes, that my twelve years in the army had brought me so little. The empty restaurant seemed to fit with the emptiness I felt in my own life.

I sat down at a table near the window and began examining the menu.

"May I help you, sir?" I heard a soft voice ask—a voice with just the faintest trace of the South in it. I looked up to see a small, slender young girl in a waitress' uniform. Her long, curly hair was almost gold, her eyes were large and green. She seemed shy; she would look at me for only a moment and then her eyes would dart off in another direction. And she had big dimples and a nervous little laugh, as I discovered when I offered up some trivial pleasantry. As she walked back to the kitchen to give the cook my order, I detected a slight limp. She seemed very young and somehow fragile.

When she returned with my steak, I asked her her name.

"Wanda. Wanda Klossing," she said, hesitantly. Each time I looked at her she seemed younger than she'd seemed before.

"How old are you?" I asked.

"Seventeen." She barely looked at me.

"Seventeen!" I said. "You must still be in high school."

"That's right. I'm a senior." I could see she was a

little afraid of me, but I would not be put off. Suddenly, my loneliness seemed to have become insupportable; I wanted to talk with someone.

"My name's Orville Kelly. But I'd rather be called 'Kelly' than 'Orville.' Where are you from? You don't sound like an Iowan."

"I was born in Alabama—Tuscaloosa. But I've lived in Burlington for nearly nine years." Her eyes wandered to my uniform. "How long have you been in the army?"

"About twelve years."

"Do you get to travel?"

"Sure," I said. "I've been to Japan, Korea, France, Germany, the Marshall Islands. I'll be going back to Korea in a few days."

Her eyes lit up at the names of these foreign places. I was touched by her youth, her freshness and simplicity.

"Gee, I've always wanted to travel. There's not very much to see in Burlington. I've thought about joining the WACs when I get out of high school."

The door opened and an elderly couple came in.

"Excuse me, Mr. Kelly," the girl said, and she hurried off to take their order.

My eyes followed her. I knew I was attracted to her, but I really wasn't sure why. I just had the feeling that she needed someone big and strong to hold her and protect her, and I wanted to be that someone. In spite of the difference in our ages; in spite of the difference in our ways of life.

"May I walk you home after work?" I asked her when she brought me my check.

She hesitated for a moment, her eyes wide open. She seemed frightened, and I fully expected her to turn me down. But she didn't.

"I guess it will be all right," she said.

I did most of the talking on the six-block walk to her parents' home. I told her about Yokohama and Paris and all the other foreign cities I had visited. She seemed fascinated by my travels, but she was reluctant to tell me much about herself. All I learned that evening was that her father was an ironworker and that her mother was a beautician. That accounted for her beautiful hair.

When I left her, I went straight back to my hotel room and lay awake for an hour or more, thinking about her. I felt as if I was back in high school myself: I felt like a schoolboy trying to impress a pretty girl. That was a feeling I hadn't had in a long time. None of the many girls I'd known since I'd been in the army had been as reticent or as trusting as this slender little seventeen-year-old.

The next evening, I found myself returning to Tiny's. When she saw me, a big grin came to Wanda's face. The weather had turned chilly, and when I walked her home I gave her my army coat to wear over her shoulders. It felt good to be doing even that small thing to protect her. This time, she told me a little more about herself: that she was glad to be finishing with school, and couldn't wait until she graduated; that she wanted to do something new and interesting, but didn't know what. I remember laughing to myself when she said that. I had felt the same way when I was in high school.

I don't really know, even now, whether I'd already fallen in love with Wanda. But I do know that I felt I needed her and that she needed me. I needed someone who could help me feel that I was worth something again; ever since Japtan, I'd been feeling pretty worthless. I wasn't sure what Wanda needed, but somehow I felt that I could be a help to her. And now I was on my way to Korea. We might never see one another again. I couldn't let that happen. Even though we'd known one another such a short time, I had a feeling we belonged together.

The next day, I counted the hours until I knew Wanda would be home from school. Then I picked up the telephone and dialed her number. I was very nervous. But I had made up my mind that I couldn't lose her.

"Hello, Wanda. This is Kelly. How are you?"

"Fine, thanks." Her voice sounded startled and a little worried. "Is something wrong?"

"No, not at all." I paused and took a deep breath. "Will you marry me?"

"What?" she sounded incredulous.

"I said: 'Will you marry me?' "

"You're kidding," she said, with a slight laugh.

"No. I mean it. Will you marry me?"

The silence at the other end of the phone was deafening.

"I don't know. I mean, I'll have to think about it. Are you sure this isn't some kind of joke?"

"It's no joke. I want to marry you."

"Well, I'll have to think about it."

My heart fell.

"I'll tell you tomorrow."

I still had a chance!

"I'll call you after school, then."

"Yes, do that."

Four days later—October 24, 1959—Wanda and I were married at the Oak Street Baptist Church in Burlington. I had met her parents two days earlier. Her father had given us his consent quite willingly, but her mother was at first reluctant. I really can't blame her. None of the Klossings knew much about me—just that I was a soldier in the U.S. Army, on my way to Korea. I hadn't told them anything about my childhood, my family, Toshyko, Eniwetok, the AWOL. I was afraid to; if they knew, they might send me packing. And I didn't want that.

Our honeymoon was over almost before it began. We had two weeks together in Burlington and then I was shipped off to Korea. It was rough on both of us, Wanda especially. I had hoped to be able to make arrangements for her to follow me to Korea, but the army bureaucracy was rigid, labyrinthine, and unbeatable. Even if, in time, I'd been able to fight my way through the red tape to make the necessary arrangements, I'd still have had to scrap them. Wanda discovered she was pregnant. And that ruled out any possibility of her coming to join me.

Our letters to one another were exchanges of loneliness. Wanda felt estranged from all her old high school friends. They were concerned with their studies and with having good times; she was concerned with the life she felt growing inside her. She finally decided to leave school and go back to Tuscaloosa to live with her grandmother, at least until the baby was born. My situation was, at first, a little better. I'd only been in Korea a couple of months when I became a radio announcer with the Armed Forces Korea Network. "Music With Sergeant

Kelly." I had my own country and western show, with a little pop music thrown in. I thought I had a good chance to earn back my sergeant's stripes and prove, once again, that I was a good army man. But the army had other ideas. It claimed that I'd been overpaid during part of my enlistment, and began deducting the overpayment from my monthly check. That left me with barely enough to support myself. And I had to be able to support Wanda, also, and the baby, when it came. I tried borrowing, to see if I could work things out that way. But that was no good either. It simply increased the number of my creditors.

Finally I went to my commanding officer for advice. He suggested that I leave the army, and said he would recommend me for an honorable discharge. That way, I could go back to the States, take up a civilian occupation, and support my wife and family. It seemed the best idea. Wanda and I missed each other. I'd lost my enthusiasm for the army. I agreed to leave.

My discharge papers came through. Stamped on them was the word "undesirable." No one ever explained to me why that word was there. I presume it had something to do with the money the army said I owed it. But, if that was the case, the money—it seemed to me—should have been weighed against my twelve year record, which had on it only one blot:

the AWOL. And which included commendations and medals and access to top-secret material. I was bitter and disgusted. But I had to get out of the army. And by now I was ready to.

Ironically enough, that army discharge was changed to "honorable" about twelve years later, shortly after I discovered I had cancer. I started applying for this change almost immediately after I left the army, but it took all that time to go through.

And that word "undesirable" *was* a stigma. It cut me off from any number of jobs. The ones I was able to get didn't satisfy me. I was used to more authority, and more status. I did some stenography work. I sold cars and later encyclopedias. I worked as a collection agent.

Even if the jobs had been no problem, I'd have found it difficult to adjust to a settled civilian life. I was used to living in a barrack full of men, to a life without any deep emotional attachments or any real emotional responsibility for any other human being. In fact, it wasn't until the birth of Lori, our third child, that I was finally able to deal with the emotional demands of family life and that I finally came to realize how deep and satisfying its rewards are.

The first months of my return must have been

very hard on Wanda. I wanted to spend my evenings doing what I'd always done in the evenings when I was in the army: going out drinking. And that's what I did—leaving her alone in the small apartment we found in Burlington. We quarreled often, and once, when I'd stayed out drinking until three in the morning, she didn't speak to me for two days. And then she had to put up with the shock of discovering I'd been anything but a saint during my years in the army: I'd let things slip when I had too much to drink, and there were photographs and other mementos that I'd kept. It couldn't have been easy for her—by now eighteen and well into her pregnancy—a young, romantic, and naive girl who'd seen no more of life than there was to be found in Tuscaloosa, Alabama, and Burlington, Iowa.

But Wanda is the most tolerant and understanding person I've ever met, and she fought to make our marriage a real marriage. She looked ahead, and not back. We started our life together as strangers; but by the time Mark was born, we knew each other pretty well and had gotten to love one another deeply.

Mark's birth helped me settle down a little bit. No longer did I want to spend my evenings away from my family, drinking with other men. I found my son and my wife far better company than anyone else I knew. But I was still restless. The habits of my wandering childhood and my years in the army died hard. Wanda, Mark, and I moved around a great deal, up and down the Mississippi River, in Iowa and Illinois, anywhere I thought I could find a job. We were still moving when Tammy came, and then Lori, and there were five mouths to feed.

I thought I was taking my responsibilities seriously. But I wasn't. I wasn't satisfied with the kinds of jobs I could get, and I was uprooting my family in search of that satisfaction. It took a miserable winter on a small farm we had rented outside Davenport, Iowa, to bring me to my senses—a winter so cold and desolate that some of our ducks froze to death overnight. When I looked out the kitchen window, I saw them standing stiff and lifeless in the yard.

The sight of those ducks somehow drove the point home to me. I had promised myself, when I was young, that when I got married and became a father, I would provide my children with the safe and steady home life I had never known. I wasn't doing it. I wasn't really being a much better father to them than my grandfather or my uncle Willie had been to me. I was putting them—and Wanda—through a lot of needless pain and suffering for the sake of my ego. I made up my mind that I would have to become a real father to my children and a real husband to my wife. I would have to make a full and genuine commitment to my family and to my responsibility as the head of the house.

We left the farm and moved into Davenport, where I supported the family by doing odd jobs. There was nothing glamorous about the work I got to do. But it paid the bills and that was enough for me.

Then I heard that there was a job available in the nearby town of Sterling, Illinois, as a newspaper reporter. I'd never had any experience in the newspaper business, but I'd always liked to write, and I didn't think I'd have anything to lose by looking into it. So I drove to Sterling and had a talk with the editor. The interview left me feeling dejected. It really drove home to me my lack of qualifications for the job. When he asked me to call him in a couple of days to learn his decision, I thought he was just being polite; trying to let me down gently. So I didn't call.

A few days thereafter, a messenger arrived at the house with a letter. It was from the editor of the Sterling newspaper. He wanted me to come to work for him. I owe that man a good deal. I've never been a polished writer, and I had a lot to learn about newspapers. But I enjoyed learning and I enjoyed the hectic atmosphere of a newspaper office. For the first time since I'd left the army, I found my work satisfying and fulfilling; I felt that I was really accomplishing something on the job. Within a year, I was promoted to city editor. But more importantly, I could honestly say that I was providing a steady home life for my family.

In the next years, we moved several times for other newspaper jobs with other challenges. But it was the job at Sterling that gave me, for the first time, the sense that there was a direction to my working life. I felt like a new person—in more ways than one. The byline "Orville Kelly" sounded pretty drab to me, so I decided to use my middle name, Eugene, abbreviated to Gene. The readers of the papers I worked for knew me as Gene Kelly. If I hadn't gotten sick, I'd be Gene Kelly still—a newspaperman in some midwestern town, living a quiet, uneventful life with my family.

THREE

Nothing could have prepared me for all the things that began to happen within a few weeks of the first meeting of Make Today Count. I simply did not understand the ramifications of the event: that, in looking for a way to make the most of the time I still had ahead of me, I had brought out into the open a problem that was tormenting thousands of people and that, in sitting down to talk with seventeen other men and women whose lives had been turned upside down by cancer and by the fear of death, I had started a movement that would spread throughout the United States.

How could I have realized? There's nothing, after all, particularly new about the idea of making each day count. Philosophers and theologians have been urging us to do this ever since the beginning of recorded history. And I'm certainly no messiah, ordained to show the public the light. I get very little satisfaction from comments like the one a middle-aged Illinois woman made to me, after I'd finished speaking one Sunday at her church.

"God must have chosen you to have cancer, Mr. Kelly," she said, gazing earnestly at me. "He wanted people to hear the message, and He elected you to do the work."

"I wish He'd elected someone else," I told her. And I meant it.

Even more, it simply never occurred to me that what we in Burlington were doing was in any way unusual. As a matter of fact, if I had been asked, at that time, to characterize our group, I'd have described it as a second best—a make-do technique we had to resort to because we lived in a small, relatively unsophisticated city. If we lived in a large metropolitan center—in New York or Chicago or Los Angeles—all kinds of professional help would be offered us in dealing with the emotional problems we were facing. The big cities, I felt sure, were handling the entire matter much more openly and much more humanely.

I was, as it turned out, dead wrong. Metropolitan centers weren't handling our emotional and psychological problems any better than small cities or towns. Like the small cities and small towns, they weren't handling them at all. The health professionals were dispensing medication—or providing other treatments; talking honestly—or evasively—with patients; treating patients with kind—or brusque—efficiency. They were dealing with their patients' medical problems. Period. Paragraph. The end. The void I'd felt in the handling of my case—the complete lack of any help toward emotional rehabilitation—was one that almost every other cancer patient felt also. It was a problem, as I later discovered, of which thoughtful people in the health professions were already aware.

A Texas physician wrote me, after Make Today Count had become widely known: "I personally think that this type of venture should have been undertaken years ago by the hospitals in their consulting services. Aside from the diagnosis and treatment of various carcinomas and sarcomas, I'm afraid the medical profession has not done much in regard to looking at the whole individual and seeing how we can give him aid."

And I was even more wrong in thinking that Make Today Count was a second-best way for us to cope with our problems. It was, in fact, the best way possible. The one other cancer rehabilitation group I know of—Reach For Recovery—is made up of women who have had mastectomies and who have undertaken to help others recovering from that operation to deal with the emotional consequences of their surgery. Alcoholics Anonymous has been proving for many years now that the most effective kind of help is self-help. That's what Make Today Count is—an organization in which we learn to help ourselves by sharing with others whose problems we, too, face.

Once Make Today Count was founded, I don't think anything could have stopped it. It was, apparently, an idea whose time had come. But the speed with which it moved ahead—as of this writing, there are forty chapters throughout the country and more are being formed almost every week—still staggers me. Nor did it take much to trigger all that activity—only the account in the Burlington *Hawk-Eye* of our first meeting. Some enterprising reporters on both the Associated Press and the United Press picked up the story—perhaps because they saw its human interest, perhaps because they recognized the importance of what we were trying to do. And soon articles began to appear, about me and about Make Today Count, in other Iowa newspapers and in metropolitan dailies all across the country.

Those articles touched off a flood of letters and telephone calls—from people who were themselves confronting illness and imminent death; from friends and relatives of such people; from churches, clubs, and other groups asking me to speak. I was flattered—who wouldn't be? But I was also frightened. I am, after all, no expert. I have no training in medicine, or in psychology and philosophy. I haven't even got a college degree. My years as an army sergeant had taught me something about being a leader, but the army had also given me training in the areas in which I was to lead. I had no training in the problems of incurable illness or in the facts of death and dying. Everything I knew about those subjects I'd had to learn for myself—through months of misery of spirit and even suicidal despair. I felt completely unqualified to lead others. All I could do was tell them about my experiences and encourage them to live fully for as much time as was left to them. The things I had to say didn't strike me as particularly valuable or particularly earth-shattering. But I felt I had an obligation to say whatever I could. The people who were calling me—from all over the country and frequently collect (which put a pretty severe burden on our skimpy family budget)—saw me as someone who would listen to their problems, someone who would understand.

It was really pretty ironic: I, who less than six months earlier, had been unable to bring myself even to say the word "cancer" to my wife, was now talking about it openly with perfect strangers—

disembodied voices at the other end of the telephone. Some of those strangers undoubtedly thought I was harsh. Whenever I heard the hesitant noises and evasive words with which they were trying to avoid giving names to their fears, I would say the names for them. Cancer. Death. I knew how hard the lesson was to learn, but I knew, from my own experience, how important it was to learn it. Cancer has to be faced. Death has to be talked about openly. Our society doesn't do it; we prefer to sweep unpleasant subjects under the rug. But those of us who live in the knowledge of our deaths cannot afford to do this. We must give a name to our fears. Only that way can we keep ourselves from thinking of nothing *but* death. Only that way can we free ourselves from being obsessed by it. Only that way can we give ourselves a chance to take pleasure in our daily lives, and give our lives some sense of meaning and accomplishment.

Less than two weeks after the appearance of the first wire-service story about Make Today Count, something happened that gave me more confidence in my own intuitions. I discovered that those intuitions coincided with the expert knowledge of a group of specialists I'd never even heard of before —thanatologists: psychologists and psychiatrists whose special field is the study of death and dying. It came about as a result of one of those long-distance phone calls—this time, not collect. The caller was the producer of the "Tomorrow Show," a late-night network television program that was planning to do a segment on death and dying. One of the participants would be Herman Feifel, a professor of psychology at the University of Southern California whose special field was thanatology. Would I be willing to fly to Burbank to take part in the program, together with Dr. Feifel and Tom Snyder, the host? You bet I would be. I had learned things—both through my own experience and through the experiences that had been reported to me in the letters and phone calls I was getting—that I wanted to say to the whole country about the way we handled this problem. And I was interested to hear what the experts felt.

"The one thing that keeps coming up in all the letters and phone calls I've been receiving," I said at one point in the discussion, "is that something is wrong with our approach to death and dying. We have surrounded it with fear and unnecessary mystery."

Dr. Feifel, to my great pleasure, said much the same thing.

"Dying is not a very happy circumstance in America these days," he said. "And it can be less dehumanizing than it is. Everyone is scared of death —of the unknown. It's the end. The end of everything. No more chances. No more possibilities. And it's not just the average guy who's frightened. So are the professionals in health care—the doctors, nurses, even the clergy.

"One of the reasons, I think, is that we avoid the subject of death in our culture. We no longer command religious philosophies or conceptual creeds with which to transcend death. Death has become a wall for us. It is no longer a doorway, as it was for our grandparents. And in a society like ours in America, which worships the future so much, the prospect of no future at all is an abomination.

"Hence there is a tremendous hostility against and repudiation of death. And this is true in the health professions. Once a person is determined to be terminally ill, and is in the hospital, the doctors increase their attention to his physiological needs. The dying person activates our own fear of death—which we can't deal with—and we can't be of any help to him."

What a relief it was to hear that! If only there had been someone like Dr. Feifel at Burlington Memorial Hospital or at the University of Iowa Hospital when I was there!

That television appearance released another flood of letters—nearly all of them reflecting the same isolation and desperation I once had felt. No one could have read them without wanting to help, even if the only help there was to offer was a letter of friendship and encouragement.

"Things just seem to be getting harder all the time," wrote the divorced mother of a six-year-old son, who had recently learned she had cancer. "My moods go up and down like a Yo-Yo. I find myself screaming at my son for no reason at all. I've thought of suicide. I need a friend right now who knows how I feel. Please write."

"I'm terminally ill," wrote another woman. "I have incurable cancer. Sometimes I break out in a cold sweat when I think of dying. What can I do?"

There were others—hundreds of them—not only from patients but from their friends and relatives. A few told happier stories—of people who had learned to deal openly with their feelings; of diseases diagnosed as incurable that had, with treatment, gone into long periods of remission. Others asked for advice on how to start chapters of Make Today Count.

But in spite of all the mail that was pouring in, in spite of the fact that it had become a full-time job for me just to answer it, I still didn't grasp the full import of what was happening. As an ex-newspaperman, I knew the power of the media—not merely to inform, but also to inflate—to create what we call pseudo events: those stories that have vanished from even the back pages only two days after they were announced in banner headlines on page one. I was, I guess, something of a cynic. Even though I knew the need was real and widespread, I took it for granted that when all the media publicity about me and about Make Today Count had died down, both I and the organization would fall back into the obscurity from which we had so suddenly emerged. So for the first few months, I continued answering the letters the postman brought daily—assisted now by members of a stenography class at Burlington High School—expecting that momentarily they'd stop coming.

But they didn't. If anything, they increased in volume. And more and more of them—both from health professionals and from cancer victims and their families—were requests for information on how to form chapters of Make Today Count.

By June of 1974—six months after that first meeting at the Burlington Elks Club; a year after my cancer had been diagnosed—it became apparent that we could no longer continue on such a slapdash basis. Already there were more than twenty Make Today Count chapters—some of them with as many as seventy members. We needed to be able to keep one another informed of what we were doing; we needed a central clearinghouse. So, on the advice of my attorney, we applied for a federal charter as a nonprofit, tax-exempt corporation in the State of Iowa. That would enable us to solicit funds to pay necessary expenses—and by now, those necessary expenses included a secretary. The charter was granted. The little studio next to my bedroom became our national headquarters; our dining room the meeting place for our nine-man board of directors, made up, to begin with, of members of our local Make Today Count chapter—both cancer victims and others: a minister, a lawyer, and a man to whom we owe a special debt of gratitude—Dr. Carl Hulen, a Burlington resident who contributed most of the money we so desperately needed to get Make Today Count off the ground.

According to its charter, Make Today Count is made up of two groups of people. Patients and their families or survivors—and by patients we mean not only cancer victims, whether their prognosis is favorable or unfavorable, but also victims of other serious incurable diseases—are the central core, the members proper. In addition, we have associate members—physicians, nurses, nursing students, ministers, social workers, college students—anyone interested in the work we are doing and willing to learn, to share, and to help. There are no dues; the only requirement to maintain membership in good standing in Make Today Count is attendance at meetings.

Those meetings—informal gatherings, usually held once a month—are the heart of our program, the best therapy we can offer one another. Our main concern is the sharing that takes place—the sharing of feelings by both sick and healthy people seeking ways of coping with the emotional traumas of illness, and ways of growing in their appreciation of daily life. But chapter meetings are also used to hear guest speakers—physicians, nurses, clergymen, lawyers, psychiatrists—anyone who has knowledge or information that can be helpful to the terminally ill and their families. Sometimes the meetings are purely social: members get together for a potluck dinner, or a picnic or holiday party.

But before Make Today Count can help anyone, that person must have decided that he or she wants to be helped. That want is a *sine qua non.* Make Today Count meetings are not exercises in self-pity or competitions for the "loser" prize. We do not sit around commiserating with one another. But because, in our society, people who are seriously ill are frequently verbally oppressed—afraid or unable to speak openly about their feelings—the first step each person has to take is to admit those feelings. Cancer and other incurable diseases can—and do

—change our lives and our relationships with our families and with the community, isolating us from the rest of society. If Make Today Count is to accomplish its purpose—to become a gateway back into the mainstream of life for those whose lives have been shattered by illness—its members must be willing to be open in discussing their problems and their experiences.

And when they *are* open, it can make a major change in their lives. None of the people I've met proved this truth to me more dramatically than the young woman—no more than twenty-six—who wrote me, in suicidal despair, soon after her cancer had been diagnosed.

"I've got no reason to go on living, Mr. Kelly," her letter said. "My marriage is miserable. When my husband lost his job, about a year ago, he began to drink and to become abusive. I only stayed with him because I thought things would get better once he got back to work. But he still hasn't got a job—and the way he is now, I doubt he'll ever be able to get one. And he's become nearly as ugly to the children as he is to me.

"Now I've learned I have cancer and I don't have much more time. So it makes no sense at all for me to go on. I'm going to take the children to California, to my parents, and I'm going to leave them there. And then I'm going back home, and I'm going to take some pills and get it all over with. That's the only choice I've got."

That letter scared me. I knew I had to act. But I was afraid a letter might not reach the young woman quickly enough, and, even if it did, it might not be sufficiently persuasive. So I tracked down her phone number—she lived in Missouri—and, after a half hour's conversation, managed to persuade her to bundle her children into her car and drive to Burlington with them.

The strain that she and her children had been living under was evident from the moment they walked through our door. Her two older boys—three and five—had tension written all over their faces. And the baby—nine months old—looked like a little old man.

Wanda swept up the kids to play with Britty and Lori and I marched the mother into my studio. It took me three hours to persuade her to come to the Make Today Count meeting we were having that evening. But I finally managed.

The meeting made the difference. Listening to others, in the same position as she, speak openly and honestly about their feelings and seeing that, in spite of their illness, they were living their lives hopefully, from day to day, brought hope to our young friend. When she left Burlington the next day, it was with the promise that she'd keep in touch, and that, when she got home, she would make it her business to get a chapter of Make Today Count started in her home town. She kept her promise. I still hear from her about once a month. She's doing fine. And the chapter of Make Today Count that she founded is one of the strongest ones we now have.

As Make Today Count has grown, so have our activities and our plans. Several of the chapters have organized programs of visits to hospitals and to the homes of persons too ill to attend meetings. Our Iowa chapters have been asked to provide rehabilitation suggestions for cancer patients as part of a statewide cancer control program. To keep the thousands of Make Today Count members abreast of our activities, we publish a monthly newsletter. We are currently at work producing an information packet consisting both of printed matter and of cassette tapes, which offers hints as to how to form an MTC chapter; suggestions of ways to assist patients and their families with their emotional problems; and interviews with families who have advice as to how, sensitively and compassionately, to break the dread news of terminal illness.

On January 5, 1975, the Burlington chapter of Make Today Count held its first anniversary party.

Naturally, it was at the Burlington Elks Club, in the very same room in which we had met the year before. It was a bittersweet occasion—a time to be proud of the success of Make Today Count, a time to relax and chat with old and new friends, a time to make plans for the future. And a time to notice that, of the dozen cancer patients who had been at our first meeting, only two were still alive.

In June 1974, at about the same time we were granted our charter, Make Today Count got its second big publicity spurt. The CBS program "60 Minutes" did a segment on us. It had actually been taped back in February, during the snowy Iowa winter. For three dizzying days, the film crew had followed me and my family virtually everywhere we went. They had accompanied me to Iowa City, and filmed me as I was having a chemotherapy treatment. They had traveled with Wanda and me to Fairfield, Iowa, to a meeting of Make Today Count. They had filmed every inch of our house and every one of its inhabitants—from Wanda and me and the kids to our cats and dogs. If we weren't tripping over wires, we were tripping over cameramen.

I still remember part of the exchange between me and Mike Wallace, who interviewed me. He had asked me about the Make Today Count philosophy, and I had told him something about my feeling that too many people waste their lives—seeing things but not noticing or appreciating them; treating time as if it had no end.

"You're not a Pollyanna," Mr. Wallace said in response to my comment. "I sense that you mean what you're saying. But what I find difficult to understand is how you came to that point of view."

"Well," I said, "I have my bad moments. But I feel that I'm helping people now. And that's something I never did before. I never went out of my way to help anyone. I was too busy."

"Helping yourself?" Mr. Wallace asked.

"Worrying about myself," I said. "That's very different. I find it really does something for you to become involved with other people."

That statement sums up my feelings. I honestly believe that Make Today Count and the people it has brought me in touch with have prolonged my life. They have given me a reason to get up in the morning and to continue fighting. I have lived more intensely in the months since Make Today Count was formed than in all the forty-two years before I became ill. I have learned more about myself and other people than I learned in all my army adventures in all the faraway places I dreamed of as a kid.

Most important, I have come to understand,

through experience, the real meaning of all those phrases that exhort us to care for one another—all those phrases we generally think of as pious, idealistic hopes for what ought to be, but isn't, and that we generally interpret as meaning only that *our* lives would be easier if other people cared more about *us*. The real meaning of those phrases is very different. It is that our care for other people is what gives purpose and meaning to our lives.

I didn't even begin to understand that until I was twenty-nine, when I met and married Wanda. Nothing in my uprooted childhood or my wandering army life ever showed me the true meaning of emotional commitment to other people or genuine concern for them. Until Wanda appeared, I lived in the form of solitary confinement we call self-centeredness. The birth of my children further broadened my emotional horizons. And then, when my cancer was diagnosed, I fell back into a more profound emotional isolation and self-concern than I had ever before experienced. Make Today Count is what pulled me out of it, and brought me back to life. I had no idea, when I wrote that article for the *Hawk-Eye*, that I had written myself a prescription at least as potent as those I've gotten from my physicians.

It is the knowledge of what Make Today Count

has meant for me and can mean for others that has given me the strength and energy to face the demands that have been made on me and my family since it was founded: the camera crews that have come to film us for documentaries on death and dying to be used in colleges, universities, and medical and nursing schools in this country and abroad; the punishing lecture schedule that has taken me all over the country, from San Diego to New York, to speak at more than two hundred gatherings—from meetings of twenty to thirty people in small-town churches to meetings with the National Cancer Institute, the American Cancer Society, and members of the department of psychiatry at Harvard Medical School. It has enabled me to keep relatively calm in the face of some pretty unpleasant attacks—the insinuations that I am making money by charging lecture fees, which of course is not true; the words of the newspaper reporter whose story described me as "having the time of my life" since I discovered I had cancer. I find it hard to believe that reporter would want to change places with me.

Especially now. Because, ironically enough, as the demands on me have multiplied, I grow steadily weaker physically. I can feel my energy slowly but surely draining away. My doctors have placed me on various potent drugs that, both they and I am convinced, are helping enormously to keep me alive. But their side effects are pretty unpleasant. I sleep very little, and when I do, I am often tormented by nightmares. I am becoming very irritable. The least little noise can get me extremely upset. My concentration is shot, and it's often difficult for me to keep my thoughts organized.

I know that I'm not a whole human being any longer. From the time my disease was first diagnosed, it was evident that the cancer was pretty widespread—that it had probably invaded my lungs, my liver, my spleen, an area near my kidneys and the area next to my heart. Now I live from day to day on the basis of my various body counts—the counts that indicate how I'm getting along. When I give speeches during the winter, I have to ask those in the audience with colds to move to the back of the room so I won't catch any germs. Pneumonia could be fatal to me. The drugs are fighting the cancer, the cancer is fighting to grow again, my body is fighting to regain its natural balances, the chemotherapy drugs are killing the healthy cells as well as the cancerous ones. The battle goes on. And every day, I wonder just how many more days I can make count.

The first time I was asked to speak to a college audience, I was truly startled. It had never occurred to me that young people would have any interest in such a somber subject as death. But obviously they have: There are currently about twelve hundred courses on death and dying in American colleges and universities. I had no idea of that when in April of 1974, I was asked to speak at the University of Rhode Island. I fully expected, when I accepted the invitation, that there would be no more than twenty people in my audience. So you can imagine my surprise when I found myself on the stage of a large auditorium, looking out into an audience that numbered in the hundreds. Even with such a large group, it seemed to me it would be wise to stick to my usual procedure: to make a brief opening statement about the way Make Today Count got started, and then to throw the floor open to questions. That way, I can talk about the subjects the audience is interested in. The questions that evening were like the questions I've been asked in any number of other places.

"What do you say to a dying man?" one of the students asked me.

"If you mean someone who's terminally ill, like me, I think you should say the same things you say to anyone. Just because someone has been diagnosed as incurable doesn't mean that they've lost all their interest in everything. If you mean someone who's close to the end, my answer is a little different. In such a case, the first thing you have to do is learn to listen. If you listen, you'll soon learn what that person wants to talk about. And then you talk with him about those things. The things that matter to him."

"Should a cancer patient be told he has cancer?" another wanted to know.

"That's a complicated one. Most people should, I think, be told. If they know, they can take the steps necessary to adjust themselves to the enormous changes that are going to come into their lives. Because whether or not their cancer has a good prognosis, the disease itself is certainly going to affect them profoundly. And they're the ones who are going to have to deal with those effects. No one else can do it for them.

"On the other hand, there does seem to be a small number of people who are not, at first, able to cope with the knowledge of their illness. And they may have to be told very slowly and gradually and even more gently than usual. I think we have to be honest about cancer and honest about death. But not brutal."

"Do you believe in God?" from a third student. And after I'd answered that I do, another question, from a fourth: "How can you believe in God? You can't see Him or touch Him. How can you believe?"

"Well, you know, I love my wife and children very deeply, but I can't reach out and put my hand on that love. And in the spring, I can feel the breeze brush my cheek, but I can't reach out and grab the breeze and hold it in my hand. I can hear a newborn baby's cry in the hospital, and I feel the presence of God."

The questions went on and on: I could see the students really cared about the things we were discussing. Nor did the interest stop when the session was finally over, when the last public question had been asked and answered. Then, a small knot of students moved hesitantly to the podium; obviously, each of them had a personal problem to discuss. I noticed then—as I had noticed before and would notice in the future—that there were more women in the group than men. Women seem to be more willing to deal openly with emotional problems than men. And that resistance of my sex to emotional honesty is one of the problems Make Today Count still faces. The number of men among our membership is increasing. But women are still in the majority. I won't feel satisfied that I've done my job properly until I can see the same openness among men as among women in facing the problems of serious illness and death.

But let me get back to my story—to that little knot of students who came up to talk with me, each of them drawing me aside in turn, so that our conversation could be private.

The first to speak was an Oriental girl in her late teens. Her cheeks were smudged with tears.

"Mr. Kelly, my father died a month ago from lymphoma. I loved him so much. I don't seem to be able to get over it." She looked at me and then looked down at the floor. Her need to unburden herself was so strong it was almost palpable. And so, evidently, was her shame that she could not control her feelings.

"He didn't want to die, Mr. Kelly," she went on. "And we didn't want to lose him. We wanted him to live."

"Of course you did," I said. "I don't want to die, and I know my family doesn't want me to die either. But it seems that that's what's going to happen. You know, I have two daughters, a little younger than you are. I often wonder what their lives will be like after I die. I know what I want for them: I want them to be happy, and to find the things that will bring fulfillment to their lives. I don't want their lives to stop just because mine did. And I'm sure your father felt as I do."

"We loved him so much, though."

"Of course you did. And it's natural for you to feel grief. But I know your father wouldn't want you to let that grief consume your life."

The girl tried to speak. She couldn't. I could see she still didn't feel strong enough to face her grief alone.

"Where's your mother?" I asked.

"She's at home. In Boston. She feels the same way I do."

"Why don't you go home to her for a while, then? You could help each other."

She looked up at me. "Do you think I should?" she asked. "I was afraid it would only make her feel worse if I was around."

"Do you really think so? Or do you think you'd try to help each other get over your grief and back to a normal life?"

"We *would* try to help one another, wouldn't we? If we were together for a little while, we might both feel better."

There was gratitude in her voice; apparently, it had helped her just to talk.

"Mr. Kelly?" the next girl started. "I'm sorry to bother you. I won't take but a minute of your time." She was in her early twenties and very attractive, with wavy auburn hair. "It's about my mother. You see, she just told me she has cancer. I'm not sure what to do. I think I should quit school to be with her, but I don't know which way to turn. What do you think I should do?"

"Is the cancer in its early stages?"

"Yes."

"Have you asked your mother what she would like you to do?"

"Well, not exactly." The girl seemed startled. "I don't like to say too much about it because I'm afraid of upsetting her."

"Don't you think you should talk it over with your parents before dropping out of school?"

"Well, yes—I guess so."

"Tell your parents how you feel and go from there. All three of you have to talk to one another."

The answer was a simple one, maybe too simple. But sometimes we need a little push to do things. Sometimes we want others to make decisions for us.

The next girl to come up to the stage was also in tears. She was no older than twenty, heavy-set, dressed in jeans. We were by now the only persons left in the auditorium.

"Mr. Kelly, I guess you're the first person I've ever told," she said. "I—I have cancer, too. I'm scared, Mr. Kelly. I'm scared. I haven't even begun to live. It wasn't worth it to be born."

Her words echoed in the empty auditorium. I looked into her eyes and saw terrible loneliness.

"You haven't told your parents yet?"

"No."

"Do you plan to?"

"Well, I heard what you said tonight about being open and honest, but my parents wouldn't understand. They're so emotional, anyway. I don't think they could handle it."

"You might be surprised. What happens when you get really sick? Do they fall apart?"

"No, they don't. But . . ."

I could see from her hesitation that she was far from convinced. I said, "The smartest thing I ever did was to tell my family. Do your parents live close to the campus?"

"About a hundred miles."

"Why don't you go home one weekend soon? You're going to have to tell them eventually, and you should tell them in person. It's going to be difficult, I know. But I bet they'll thank you for telling them."

"How can I be sure?"

"You can't be. But the odds are with you."

I put my arm around her as we walked toward the door. She was terribly alone. And so very young. I gave her my address and told her to write me after she had spoken to her parents. She thanked me; we parted, and I walked to my motel room, exhausted and depressed. All these girls were so young. Too young to have their lives torn up. And the last one looked a little like Tammy. How would I react, I wondered, if one of my children were ever to get cancer? I couldn't wait to lie down and try to sleep. But first I would call Wanda and talk to her, if only for a short time. That would help me push the thought of death out of my mind. And I wanted desperately to do that.

Talking to Wanda has always helped me. Even if we talk about nothing more important than the evening's dinner menu. Over the years, we've grown closer and closer and have grown to need each other more and more. That scares me. I sometimes think that Wanda loves me almost too much. It can't be easy for her now. She's as much a part of Make Today Count as I am; and in addition to all the responsibilities that entails, she's even more devoted than she ever was to our four kids.

Wanda is shy and quiet; her reticence is one of the things that drew me to her when we met. But even though she's really a very private person, she's had to learn, in the last years, to overcome her natural impulse to take a back seat. On several occasions, when I was too ill to fulfill a speaking engagement, Wanda has gone in my place; she even spoke before a national convocation of leaders in the field of death and dying. She gets nervous, but she's a most effective speaker. Everyone who hears her knows she's speaking from her heart. Although it's not always easy to persuade her of that. She's always felt a little inferior because she didn't graduate from high school. But today, even with all our difficulties, she's taking correspondence courses that will earn her a high school diploma. And she wants to go on to college some day.

It was in part an effort to repay my debt of love to Wanda, in part an effort to bring some pleasure to her during a time of great difficulty, that I accepted an invitation from the producer of a television program called "Girl of My Life" to appear with Wanda on the show. I kept it all a secret from her, and got her to accompany me to Los Angeles, where the program originated, by telling her I had a speaking engagement there and wanted her along for company.

Everyone who watched that show saw Wanda blush in living color as I read my tribute to her:

"I have spent fourteen of the happiest years of my life with this incredible woman. We have shared thousands of beautiful moments growing and learning together and I somehow knew that our children would be just like her.

"She is a woman whose name will never be included in a book of outstanding achievements, but she has more compassion, character, and common sense than anyone I've known in my lifetime.

"Oh, she does have her weaknesses! Stray dogs and cats seem to find their way to our house uninvited, for a free handout. Like the old traveling hoboes of the past, they must have a way of marking homes like ours.

"If I had been a pharaoh in ancient Egypt or a king of the past, I would have erected a monument in her memory. But I am just an ordinary man, and that monument is in my heart.

"Sometimes at night, when sleep comes hard, I awaken her to talk to her for just a little while. She is always there willing to help, to comfort, or just to listen to me.

"She has been more than any man could ask for. Her energy is boundless and I have seen her love and her laughter turn a house into a warm and loving home. Her care and her devotion have helped our children grow into happy, understanding, and intelligent young Americans, and each day they, too, count their blessings.

"My hopes were that we would grow old and watch the seasons pass together, but as we all know life is a fragile thing.

"The doctors have told me that an incurable disease will take my life someday, but I am not afraid because I believe there is a life after death and there certainly must be a place reserved for my wife and me, and my children."

Even Wanda had to admit that it had been worth the embarrassment when she discovered our prize for being on the program: a week's trip to the Virgin Islands. We'd never had a honeymoon; Wanda had always wanted one; I had always felt bad that I hadn't been able to offer it to her.

We left for St. Thomas on a rainy day in May. I felt tired and ill. I hadn't yet recovered from the effects of a week-long speaking trip, and I'd just returned from Iowa City, where I'd had one of my periodic chemotherapy treatments, which always leave me tense and wakeful for a couple of days. But I would have felt much worse if I'd permitted my exhaustion to interfere with a trip Wanda was looking forward to with such excitement—not only as a long-delayed honeymoon, but also as a chance to remove ourselves, if only for a while, from our daily problems and from the looming shadow of death.

Our hotel room was large and comfortable, and from its windows we could see the blue-green bay and the shining white sands of the beach. For the first day or so, everything was fine. But then the pall began to descend. First of all, we missed the children. Never before, in all our years of marriage, had we taken a vacation without them. Then, there were the effects of my illness. I didn't have enough energy to sight-see by day and party by night, so we had to restrict ourselves to daytime activity. And there's something rather lonely about spending one's evenings in a hotel room, no matter how comfortable and no matter how lovely the view. And even though we were together. It just somehow felt wrong. Worst of all, there was the knowledge that this was our last fling; that we would never again have another opportunity like this. A letter that one of my doctors had written in case of emergency described my illness in clinical detail. And I had to carry that depressing reminder with me constantly.

But we did our best to enjoy ourselves. And to some extent, we succeeded. For Wanda, it was a pleasure just to be able to swim in the gentle waters and to sunbathe on the shining, clean beach. And every time I looked out at the sea from the window, I felt glad to be alive.

In the middle of our week's stay we signed up for a day-long "champagne cruise" to Tortola, one of the British Virgin Islands about two hours from St. Thomas. The day dawned bright and sparkling, and Wanda and I congratulated each other for having thought of taking this excursion. The six other couples with whom we were sailing were just as enthusiastic as we were; it was as if all of us were kids, being taken to our first Treasure Island. The day was glorious—the sky cloudless, and the breeze just strong enough to offset the heat. The boat seemed to glide along the water, barely touching the waves. The passengers were chatting, laughing, pointing out the sights to one another. One couple, a man and wife in their early forties, who had introduced themselves as being from Detroit, was scurrying around the deck, taking snapshots of everything and everybody. Of all of us, they seemed the most excited to be taking the trip.

At about noon, we lowered anchor a few hundred yards from Tortola, and most of the passengers changed into bathing suits for a quick dip before lunch. I wasn't up to swimming, and Wanda had decided to remain on board with me. We were sitting on deck relaxing when suddenly we heard the frantic shouts of one of the women, screaming for help. When we caught sight of her in the water, we could see that she was thrashing wildly with one arm and, with the other, trying to keep the limp body of her husband from sinking.

Quickly, the captain lowered the rowboat and rowed over to the couple. He got the man into the boat, helped the woman in, and rowed back to us. The man was conscious, but frightened; he had apparently suffered a mild heart attack.

The noise and the excitement had brought the other passengers back to the schooner. Everyone was tense; no one said a word. As I looked around, I sensed that something was still wrong. One of the passengers was missing—the man from Detroit, the one who'd been so busy taking photographs. I went up to his wife and spoke as gently as I could.

"Your husband is still swimming, I guess."

She nodded. "He wanted to swim all the way to the island," she said. "He probably didn't hear all the noise."

Together, we went to the rail and looked out toward Tortola. But all there was to see on the water was a floating piece of driftwood. And there was no one on the beach.

It took the captain and the mate nearly fifteen minutes to find the body. All that time, the woman sat in stony silence, Wanda and I on either side of her. Not until the captain had returned to the schooner and told her what we'd all feared did she say anything. And when she spoke, her words were lifeless.

"He always wanted to make this trip," she said, over and over.

After she had been led downstairs to the cabin, the schooner started back to St. Thomas, dragging behind it the rowboat with its terrible cargo. At first, all of us sat in silence. A heart attack and a drowning. It was more than we could take in. Wanda was holding my hand as if she was afraid ever to let it go. For more than a year, my family and I had been living in the constant knowledge of my impending death. And now to confront death so brutally and suddenly—it was more than either of us could accept.

Suddenly, everyone seemed to break the silence at once. It was as if we'd all decided to call a meeting of Make Today Count. We had all seen death, and now we were looking at our lives. And all those apparently healthy people saw their lives as inadequate.

"I'm a night watchman after I get off work," said a policeman from Chicago. "I practically never get to see my kids. That's crazy. What else am I working for, except to have the pleasure of my family?"

"Our son is at college. We've grown so far apart that I'm not even sure we told him we were taking this trip," said one of the women.

"I guess I've gotten into some pretty shady business deals," one of the men said. "My conscience bothers me a lot. That's a crazy way to live—in fear of my conscience every minute."

For the two hours of our trip back to St. Thomas, a group of total strangers confided their deepest secrets to one another, huddling together to reassure ourselves that we could bring our lives more meaning than they had. We had seen how fragile life is, and how precious. That body in the rowboat behind us could have been any one of ours.

As Wanda cried herself to sleep in my arms that night, I thought back over my life—before I'd gotten cancer and since. The things I'd learned since I became ill had only been reinforced by the terrible tragedy of the "champagne cruise." That life is a gift that can be taken from us at any time. That life can only be lived from day to day and that it can only be appreciated if every moment is made to count.

For the first time, I myself began to understand

why the story of Make Today Count had so caught the public imagination—not just the imaginations of the sick, but of the healthy, too. I began to appreciate, even more than I had before, the importance it could have to its members, and my commitment to it became even greater than it had previously been. Make Today Count was three months old by this time. That night, I realized that it was my fifth child. It might still be an infant when I died, but I was going to cherish and nurture it, to guarantee its health and growth.

FOUR

The entire thrust of Make Today Count, both as a philosophy and as a movement, is to improve the quality of life for people to whom terminal illness is a real and personal matter—and those people are, of course, the terminally ill and their families. One thing, more than any other, makes it difficult to do this. That thing is the fear of death, and the fear of looking at it openly. Until we can accept the fact that death is a part of living, and that it comes inevitably to all of us, we will never be able to give meaning to the lives of those who are confronted daily by the knowledge that their own deaths—or the death of someone close to them—is an immutable, impending, and imminent reality.

A glance at any thesaurus will show you how reluctant we are to face up to death. Look under the word "birth," and you will see how many synonyms are given. Usually, there are relatively few, and all of them are pretty straightforward: *origin, creation, genesis, inception*, and *delivery*. Then look under the noun "death" and the verb "to die." The list is long, and evasions abound. After the nouns *expiration, decease, demise,* and *loss of life* come the euphemisms: *passing away, eternal rest, last breath, last gasp, last agonies, swan song, curtains, last round up, king of terrors, Grim Reaper, ultimate end, bills of mortality*. After the verbs *perish, meet one's end, be taken, rest one's breath, end one's days, cease to live, depart this life, be no more, lose one's life* come the phrases designed to take the terror from death either by making a joke of it or by using a dignified euphemism: *give up the ghost, kick off, kick the bucket, cash in, check out, croak, pop off, take a ride, sign off, pay one's debt to nature, shuffle off this mortal coil, take one's last sleep, go the way of all flesh, return to dust, cross the Styx, go to one's long account, go to one's last home, cross the bar, come to an ultimate end, go west, go out like a candle.*

The human race has spent a lot of time, and a lot of creative energy, compiling that list. But no list changes the fact that death is as natural an occurrence as birth and that, sooner or later, it comes to all of us.

Probably because I live so close to the knowledge of my own death, I have become particularly sensitive to the ways people try to deny death, and I have become increasingly convinced that this denial is not only foolish but—even worse—that it leads ultimately to a denial of life itself. I would never today permit to happen an event that occurred shortly after Make Today Count was started, when I was asked to speak before an assembly of high school students in Illinois. I told the students about our organization—about our membership and our goals —and then we threw the floor open for discussion and questions. The youngsters were extremely interested and asked many questions about ways they could help us; they seemed eager to volunteer assistance of all kinds. But not one of them asked how I felt about my own situation. Nor did a single one of them suggest that he or she ever thought about—or worried about—his or her own death. Death, it would have appeared, was a problem for me and for the members of Make Today Count. It was no problem for them.

Yet a few days later, I began to get letters from students who had been at that assembly. These letters asked questions about my feelings, or confided that the writers were fearful for themselves and concerned about their own deaths. But—all the writers explained to me—they had not raised these issues at the meeting because they found it too embarrassing.

Those letters proved to me something I had already begun to suspect: that death is something we all think about—the young, as well as the middle-aged and the old. And things that we think about deserve to be spoken about as well.

Fortunately, we are beginning to speak about death, and to investigate, scientifically, its psychological and emotional aspects. A new field has recently come into existence—thanatology, the study of death—and a new group of specialists has arisen—thanatologists. They have begun to discover the ways that people prepare themselves psychologically for their deaths, and they have also begun to understand the emotional problems that death and dying present. There is every reason to hope that this new knowledge will go far to help our entire culture deal with death more humanely than we have until now.

But for me and my family—and for hundreds of thousands like us—death and dying are something more than abstract problems. And we have no time to wait for society to reform its attitudes. We have to help one another today.

This is especially true for those of us who live in the presence of cancer. Although enormous strides have been made in its treatment, the fact remains that even today, two out of every three persons diagnosed as having the disease will die of it, even with the most expert care. And cancer is far from a rare illness. It hits one out of every three American families; next to heart disease, it is the number-one killer in the United States. In 1974 cancer killed almost 350,000 Americans; in 1975 the death rate is expected to go higher, and to reach 1,000 a day.

Nor is cancer a killer only of the middle-aged and the aged. Cancer, mainly leukemia, is the greatest disease killer of children between the ages of one and fifteen, and cancer is the leading cause of death among women between the ages of thirty and fifty-four.

Moreover, because cancer is so resistant to cure, it has become almost as dirty a word, in our society, as death. I have already described my own reluctance to tell the name of my illness to anyone—until I realized that I still had a chance to live my life for a while instead of dying inch by inch. And I still remember my early days as a newspaper reporter, when one of my jobs was to receive obituary information over the telephone from funeral directors. It was fascinating to hear them saying, after giving me the necessary information about a person who'd died of cancer:

"By the way, the family would prefer it if you

didn't use the word 'cancer' in the notice. Say he [or she] died after a lengthy illness, or extended illness, or something like that."

This conspiracy of silence among members of the family continues today. I have received any number of letters from friends and relatives of cancer patients, asking me to write to those who are ill—and requesting me not to mention the word "cancer" in my letter. Actually, I find this rather amusing. Don't these people realize that the mere fact of receiving a letter from me is likely to make the recipient suspicious, if he or she is ill? A letter I got from a man in Memphis makes this point very well.

"One of my relatives," he wrote, "sent me a copy of your newsletter. It is all about cancer. I think he is trying to tell me something. If I have cancer, instead of ulcers, as I have been told, I want to know. What disturbs me most of all now is the way my relatives, the physicians, and the nurses avoid answering my questions. If I *do* have cancer, and it is incurable, I want to know about it. There are things I want to do before I die. I feel pretty good right now, but by the time I find out the truth, I may be too sick to do anything."

Physicians, too, have been caught in this trap. Some doctors have told me they never use the word "cancer" when talking to patients. They say "malignancy" or "tumor," instead. Their rationale? So many people associate the very word "cancer" with death, that learning he or she has cancer can destroy the patient's morale. And there's no question but that some people *do* give up the battle when they learn they have cancer. I know of one woman who went into such deep despair after she learned her diagnosis that she simply lay in bed and refused to eat. She finally died—from starvation, not cancer, according to the autopsy report.

One thing is clear to me from the thousands of letters and telephone calls I have received since Make Today Count was founded. And that is that the emotional problems caused by cancer are as devastating—if not more devastating—as the physical problems caused by the disease. Very few of those letters and phone calls refer to physical suffering. They deal with mental anguish instead. For the patient, there is the fear of death and the fear of what will happen to one's family; for the family, there is the agony of standing helplessly by and the frightened anticipation of life without a loved person. There's nothing any of us can do to eliminate that anguish. Death is a fearful reality and terminal illness inevitably places an enormous strain on everyone involved. But we can at least make it our business not to add to an inevitable unhappiness.

And, from everything I've seen, the misery is compounded when family members do not share the knowledge of terminal illness with one another.

I understand the reluctance of a patient who knows of his or her illness to speak up about it. None of us wants to burden those we love with tragedy. This reluctance is expressed over and over in the letters I've gotten from people with cancer who plan to keep their illness a secret. "It will change our relationship," they write. Or: "They will pity me, and I don't want pity." Or: "I don't think they could cope with it."

It cannot be easy for anyone to cope with the knowledge that someone he or she loves has a terminal illness. But the emotional scars seem to last longer, among survivors, when they have been denied that knowledge. At an MTC seminar I conducted in Chicago, one of the women who was present told me that her daughter had died without ever having told anyone of her illness, and that she had left behind a diary which described the loneliness of a life lived in the knowledge of impending death. The girl had been dead for more than a year now, but her mother was still inconsolable in her grief.

"There were so many things we could have talked about together," she said sorrowfully to me.

In protecting her family and friends from her

own tragedy, the girl only delayed their grief and perhaps intensified it. When I looked into the mother's tearful eyes that day in Chicago, my heart ached for her unresolved sorrow—for the long work of mourning she had not yet been able to complete. She couldn't talk to a dead daughter, or do any of the things for her child that a mother would want to do. She could have talked and acted while her daughter was still living, if only she had known.

I have seen this kind of thing happen over and over. If the tragedy of terminal illness is not faced up to, openly and honestly, by everyone concerned, the burdens of grief and guilt persist far longer than they normally would.

"I did not have the heart to tell my wife, or our children," a man from New York wrote me, "that she was dying of cancer. I lied to her and told her she was ill with liver trouble, but that she would be getting better in time. She was deathly ill for six months, and died at the age of thirty-six. Not once during her months of illness did either of us speak honestly.

"Later, the worst problem was telling my children that their mother had died . . . and why. I found myself unable to deal with their anger and grief. It is two years now since my wife died, and I still haven't been able to come to terms with it. I would like to talk to people who have the same problem I do. Perhaps they can help me get over the bitterness and the self-pity I feel."

Even when both patient and family know what is happening, the conspiracy of silence may persist—all the way until the patient's death. And the survivors' guilt and mourning are thereby prolonged intolerably. One young woman wrote me that both she and her mother had known of the latter's cancer, and that she had been with her mother for every waking hour of the last two weeks of the older woman's life.

"But we never talked about anything important," said the young woman. "We talked about the weather, the past; we gossiped, we talked about clothes. But neither of us ever said what was really in our hearts, or told the other what she really felt. I still feel guilty for the time we wasted."

It was at least in part because I did not want that sense of wasted time to cloud our family's life while I was still living, or to cloud Wanda's and the children's lives after my death, that I finally decided to bring the facts of my illness into the open. And I know that other cancer patients feel as I did, and really want to speak up. Even those who write or tell me that they'd prefer to keep their condition secret. If they didn't feel the need to confide in someone, I'd never hear from them.

Even when the patient is honest, however, there is no automatic guarantee that family and friends will live up to the emotional demands of the situation. A letter I received from a woman in California makes this point abundantly clear:

"I have an incurable cancer. But that is not my problem. My problem is the negative attitude of my family and friends. My immediate family is my main concern—two wonderful sons and a husband I love dearly. My sons tolerated their father's heart surgery very well, but now that mom has cancer, they don't know how to act! I've tried for months to express my thoughts to my husband. But he shuts out what I'm saying."

And another woman, an elderly widow:

"I am a cancer patient, living a nearly normal life, probably in remission after cobalt treatment and chemotherapy. . . . The thing that makes me most angry is the way we patients are automatically treated as if we were mentally incompetent. . . . Many who have had dealings with cancer patients and their families will bear witness that the patients often face up to reality better than their relatives, yet it is the families who are consulted and obeyed. This is often a cruel refusal of civil rights; it often puts a terrible added burden on the patient, placing him in emotionally painful situations while denying him the right to live his own life. So many patients are surrounded by walls of lies and secrets just when they most need emotional support. . . .

"My worst emotional problem was finding that my family had arranged so well for my rapid deterioration that my improved health posed inconveniences for them, and threw their plans all out of line. I try to talk myself into believing that it was just a defensive gesture, facing up to the worst just as I myself might do. But it does hurt to see how inconvenient my improved condition turned out to be."

Families and friends are not the only ones who sometimes fail to deal humanely with the problems of life with cancer. During the months before I finally decided to speak openly to my family, my depression and my withdrawn behavior must have put a nearly intolerable strain on them. I simply retreated from life. I was no longer a husband to my wife or a father to my children. I was merely a ghostly presence in the house; a looming shadow. Other cancer patients punish themselves and their families in other ways.

One evening I received a long-distance phone call from a distraught woman whose husband had, she said, cancer. I couldn't always hear her clearly; there was the sound of an angry male voice in the background that sometimes drowned her out. After telling me how the cancer had been diagnosed and other details of the illness, she got to what was obviously the main point of her call.

"I can't handle him," she said. "He drinks almost constantly. It's as if he was using his cancer as an excuse to get drunk. Can you please write to him and tell him what he's doing to himself and me?"

At that moment, the husband apparently snatched the phone from his wife's hand.

"I don't want a letter, I just want another drink!" he screamed at me, and slammed down the phone.

Contrast these stories with the stories told in two letters from people who had faced up to the fact of cancer with love of others and love of life.

"I've always enjoyed my life," a cancer patient wrote me, "and I lived it quite fully up to the time I became ill. Even now, I'm living as fully and completely as possible—and getting the medication and medical help necessary to keep me functioning and relatively comfortable.

"But I do appreciate your example, which came to me at the time I needed it most. My friends have gone along with me in this attitude, now that they know how I am facing my condition. We know now in our friendship that every single day counts."

And a young wife wrote me:

"When we found out that my husband had an inoperable malignancy in the brain at age thirty-five we were stunned. It just didn't seem fair. After all those years in school he had finally gotten his Ph.D. and was a very successful research chemist for five years. We finally had gotten our first house. We have a first-grader and a pre-schooler, and were planning another child. Then our world fell apart.

"We decided the only thing to do was to live each day as best we could and, in spite of illness, life has been beautiful. Why do people say 'Don't tell a dying person'? We are so lucky to be able to make the most of what is left."

Certainly, the most sensitive and poignant situations are those that involve children. Men and women who have had long lives—who have fulfilled their obligations and commitments to their families and have seen at least some of their goals achieved—usually seem able to face death with relative equanimity. And those who survive them are usually able to accept the inevitable. But the younger a person is when death impends, the harder it is on everyone. And when a child has cancer, the strains on the parents are almost insupportable. A recent study indicates that a couple whose child has cancer is more likely than other couples to end their marriage in divorce. In one state, according to the study, the divorce rate among couples whose child had cancer was almost 80 percent! The parents tend to blame themselves and one another for the child's illness, and their mutual recriminations only exacerbate whatever problems were already present in the marriage.

"My daughter died of leukemia about three years ago," a young woman wrote me from North Carolina. "She was only six. Since then, my life has fallen apart. There was the reaction from the strain of her two-and-a-half-year illness, and there was the growing friction between my husband and me. Now that we're divorced, I begin to think we should never have married. Maybe, if she hadn't gotten sick, we could have made it. But once her illness was diagnosed, it wasn't just she, it was our marriage that was doomed. I don't know what my ex-husband felt, but I know what *I* felt: that our marriage killed our child. I know it's foolish, but I still believe that if we'd each married someone else, neither of us would have had a child with leukemia. And now, I'm frightened even to think of marrying again. I'm afraid I'll have another child who'll get sick. And I couldn't go through it again."

Many adults refuse to believe that children can accept death and dying, and they try to protect them from any knowledge of it, whether their own or someone else's. "Mommy has gone away" is the usual euphemism—which only leaves the child feeling more abandoned and deserted, and offers no comfort at all. No one would even have thought of trying to protect me in such a way when I was a youngster. Living as I did, on farms in the Midwest, I saw death close up very frequently. Dead animals were far from an uncommon sight. And people died at home, in the world that I grew up in: I saw the bodies of many neighbors, laid out in their beds. Today, most people die in institutions, away from their families and homes, and so it is easy to conceal death from the young. But I wonder how wise this concealment is. Children have vivid imaginations, and they can fantasy things far more frightening and upsetting to them than the truth.

I know that things became easier for my children after I told them about my illness. They were no longer surrounded by mystery and fear. I don't mean to suggest that they took the news without emotion. One of their first and strongest reactions was anger. "Why does it have to be *our* father?" they asked Wanda and me. We had no answer for that question, and we told them so. And our honesty has, I think, helped them accept the changes my illness has brought into our lives.

It hurts me to see the girls' sad expressions when they look at me, thinking that I don't see them. It hurts me that they're no longer free to have their friends over for noisy slumber parties. It pains me that I can no longer take Mark fishing, or play ball with him, and it pains me to see a boy who is usually a bundle of adolescent energy sitting quietly, staring into the distance—obviously sorrowing for his father and for himself. But difficult as things are for him, and for Tammy, Lori, and Britty, how much more difficult must they be for the ten-year-old girl who wrote this letter to me:

"I have cancer and I know it. But I can't talk to anyone about it. My parents won't tell me what my sickness is, and I'm not supposed to know. I think I'm going to die. I've never been to a funeral—in fact, I've never seen a dead person. Could you tell me how to die?"

Since Make Today Count was founded, I've come to know many doctors who deal, in one capacity or another, with cancer patients. On the whole, I've found them to be quite sensitive. Although I've heard some hair-raising stories of medical callousness and inhumanity, my own doctors—except for the two who misdiagnosed me before my cancer was discovered—have been uniformly decent, and all the physicians I've met on my travels have obviously wanted to be helpful and kind to their patients. But I've met many who are less than honest with their patients—primarily because they believe the patients don't want to know the truth. There may be some such people—men and women who prefer to fool themselves and to be fooled. But they are, if my experience is any indication, a distinct minority. When I speak in public, I usually ask the members of the audience to indicate, by raising their hands, whether they would want to be told the truth, if they had cancer. And regularly, anywhere from 97 to 100 percent of the audience raises its hands.

My own suspicion is that physicians who are reluctant to speak openly about cancer to their patients are as much concerned with protecting their own feelings as they are with protecting the patient's. Physicians are, after all, dedicated to preserving life. Death is their enemy, and every patient they lose is a defeat. Moreover, physicians are human beings, with all the same fears of death that the rest us have. According to one specialist in terminal cancer to whom I spoke, physicians may fear death even more than the rest of us.

"Some years ago," he told me, "I organized a conference for other doctors on death. The attendance was much smaller than I had anticipated, and many of those who were present were reluctant to speak up. Doctors seem to fear death intensely. Maybe that's why they become doctors."

Thanks to the growth of the science of thanatology, there is now a healthy trend in medical schools to include courses on death and dying, and to teach medical students how to deal, openly but sensitively, with terminally ill patients. I have been able to make some small contribution to this development by participating in training films for medical students' use.

One of the reasons it is so important for physicians to learn to deal properly with the problems of terminal illness is that they are the ones in positions of primary authority for the patient. If the doctor is reluctant to be honest with the patient, then the whole chain of command becomes reluctant to come to the patient's aid. On my travels, I have heard many complaints from nurses about this matter. Nurses are in much closer contact with hospitalized patients than are doctors. Whether patients are hospitalized for diagnosis or for treatment, the people with whom they deal most regularly and most personally are the nurses. Moreover, because the nurse does not have the aura of authority that surrounds the doctor, the patient usually feels more free to ask her questions and to reveal deep fears and concerns. But although most nurses seem to want to be open with their patients, many of them are forbidden, by the doctors, to speak.

Far worse things than mere concealment can

come from the policy of secrecy. Frequently, it is accompanied by a total lack of coordination among the members of the health team. One of the most harrowing stories I've heard was about a hospitalized cancer patient, close to death, who was visited by the hospital chaplain. The padre assumed the patient knew his condition. In fact, the patient did not. On the contrary; he'd been told he was on the road to recovery.

Imagine the agony for both of them when the chaplain opened the conversation by saying: "I know how hard this must be for you to face—the knowledge that you'll never leave the hospital."

The phenomenal growth of Make Today Count reflects many things: the need of the terminally ill to share their problems and to learn from one another; the growing willingness of our society to deal with the problems of illness and death; our growing unwillingness to tolerate cover-ups, whether political or medical. It also reflects, I think, another development: a growing independence among patients and their families—a growing refusal to place themselves passively in the hands of the experts, and to abdicate the responsibility for their own lives to the professionals. We are no longer content to be treated like children. Physicians know better than we do what the best medical treatments are for our illnesses. But we know better than they do what the best treatment is for us as human beings. That treatment is compassionate honesty.

Just as some doctors suffer from the disease of believing they know more about their patients' feelings than their patients do, so some ministers commit the sin of believing that prayer and the hope of heaven are the only comforts the sick ever need. I've told you of the ministers who came, unasked, to pray with me when my cancer was first diagnosed, and of the men of the cloth who tried to persuade me that my cancer was a blessing, not a curse. Nearly as bad are the self-ordained couriers of the Almighty, with whom I've had considerable experience.

One day, for instance, just after I'd had a chemotherapy treatment and was lying on my bed trying to rest, a man in work clothes burst into the room. He turned out to be the plumber. I had already heard the clanking of his tools while he was fixing the bathroom drain and, since I was feeling tense and disoriented, as I usually do after a treatment, the noise had grated on my nerves.

"Are you saved?" the plumber asked, peering earnestly at me.

"I think so," I answered.

"Well, it's my duty to save you again," he said, and dropped to his knees near my bed.

"Come back tomorrow," I said, and I made it a point to be unavailable when he returned.

I do not mean, by telling this story, to give the impression that I am an irreligious man. I am not an adherent of any specific denomination, but the church has been part of my life ever since I was a child. My grandmother's Bible was the first book I knew. I have spoken in church on many occasions, both before I became ill and since. Before my illness, I frequently preached as a lay minister in the congregations of several of the towns in which Wanda and the children and I lived. Since the establishment of Make Today Count, I have been asked to speak about the organization at many church services. Moreover, I *do* pray, for myself and my family. For myself, I pray that I will have the strength and the courage to make each day count; for my family, I pray that they will be able to accept my death and then go on to live their lives without me. But those prayers are my private prayers, separate from the ones I offer at church in a public company.

There are two important services, it seems to me, that ministers can perform for those who are incurably ill. They can be good listeners, and they can offer practical assistance. Those of us who know that we will soon face death are in real need of compassionate listeners. We have sorrows, we have regrets; we feel anger that our lives are going to be cut short; we fear impending pain. Even if we speak freely about these things to our families and friends, there still is likely to be more feeling bottled up inside of us; it is a help to know that we can count on men of the cloth to listen to us. And men and women who face death *do* have practical problems. The daily routine of a home is inevitably upset by the presence of cancer. Women with sick husbands may not have the time or energy to perform all the necessary household chores. Men with sick wives may find it difficult to cope with their children's demands. Ministers can help to find solutions to these real and immediate problems. Such help is much more valuable than telling someone about the beauties of heaven. The cancer patient and his family are still living on earth, and it is important for all of them to continue to find a purpose in living.

Because death is so frightening to all of us, we tend not to take care of certain practical problems related to it until we have to. I had not yet made a will when my cancer was first discovered, nor had any arrangements been made for my funeral. During the months of my despair and depression, I could not bring myself to take the necessary action. But once I was able to face my illness, I was able to face those problems, too. With less embarrassment, apparently, than some of the people with whom I had to deal.

When I called the funeral director to make arrangements for my burial, he was not in his office. I left a message for him to call me back. When he telephoned me, he hemmed and hawed and evaded the issue for several minutes. Finally, he spoke.

"I assume, Mr. Kelly," he said, "that you want to discuss the arrangements for laying you to rest."

"I'm resting right now," I told him. "I'm lying down in my den. What I want to talk about with you is what happens when I die, and how much it's going to cost."

Although medical science is now able to give years of life to many cancer patients whose disease was previously beyond the reach of any kind of treatment available, it cannot promise them any cures. And the yearning for a cure in all of us is so strong that some of us will try anything in the hope that it will help. I have no confidence in these miracle cures, and I've said so any number of times. But that hasn't prevented their advocates from pressing favorite remedies on me. A few of these treatments are probably harmless, and one of them has a certain attraction for me: I've always been fond of red wine, one of the cures that has been proposed. But it is impossible for me to believe that red wine will cure my cancer, just as it is impossible for me to believe that I will be helped by two doses of skunk oil every night; or by household ammonia (a poison!) mixed with water; or by castor oil mixed with olive oil; or by a diet of nothing but red meat and a pack of cigarettes (!) a day. I have just as little confidence in a blended mixture of two kinds of asparagus, or grape juice, or starvation, or a mixture of ground corn and wheat, or heavy dosages of vitamin and mineral supplements. Despite the impassioned letters I have received on these subjects, I cannot believe that psychic surgery can remove tumors without even breaking the patient's skin, and I have no trust in faith healing at all.

I am especially skeptical of the cure recommended to me by a man from Illinois, who made the two-hundred-mile trip to Burlington to bring me three bottles of a concoction that was, he said, a "family secret," which was, at that very moment, saving hundreds of lives in Illinois. He had, he said, improved it since its first creation, but he wasn't yet ready to submit it to the medical world for approval.

It was winter when the man came to our house, and after he left, Wanda set one of the bottles on top of the refrigerator on the back porch. When we went outside the next morning, we discovered that the cold had frozen the contents of the bottle during the night, causing the bottle to break. Wherever on the refrigerator the "cure" had fallen, the paint was completely dissolved.

If it has seemed, in some of these pages, that I do not take the knowledge of my own death seriously, that is far from the truth. It is a knowledge I live with daily. And although there is certainly no way of verifying scientifically what I am about to say, I believe that a good part of the reason I've lived as long as I have since my cancer was diagnosed is that I have wanted to live—that the knowledge of imminent death has made life very precious to me. I know that my physicians are doing everything they can for me, and I have absolute confidence in their medical judgment. But I also believe that I have a responsibility for myself, and that none of their knowledge or care can help me if I surrender to despair.

Even now, I sometimes wake up in the morning and try to reassure myself that it's all been just a bad dream. But then, when I've faced the truth, I go downstairs, out to the back porch, and watch the sun coming up over the Mississippi River. And I realize that I'm not only one day closer to death—after all, everyone's death is one day closer every morning—but that I've got another day of life in which to live.

The life I live today is based on very different values from the ones I held before I knew about my cancer. Then, material things were so important to me that I had no time to appreciate all the things that can't be bought. Now, I find more joy in the birdsong that I hear on my way to Iowa City for my treatment and in the tilled farmland I see on either side of the highway than I could in any number of material possessions. Judging from the letters I receive, many people—both sick and healthy—still see no further than the grinding round of every day; and their lives bring them very few moments of joy. But time is something we cannot take for granted. It's difficult to believe that one day the sun will rise, the birds will sing, and the world will continue—and we won't be part of it. But it remains a fact.

The greatest sin, it seems to me, is wasting God's time, and wasting our capacity to take pleasure in the simple things—a picnic with one's family, a conversation with a friend, the leaves turning, the warmth of the sun, the cool of a lakeside breeze, the sense that people care for one another.

A while ago, I received a letter from an elderly woman confined in a nursing home. "I know I am dying of cancer," she wrote, "but that isn't what bothers me. You see, my husband is in another nursing home, and we are getting ready to celebrate our wedding anniversary. We can't be together, so we are just writing to one another. I don't feel sorry for myself, but I want to tell someone about our anniversary. So I will tell you."

I took an anniversary greeting card to the next meeting of my Make Today Count chapter, and all the members signed it. A short while after we'd sent it off, another note came from the woman. "Thanks so much for the card," she wrote. "It's so nice to know you have friends."

I don't know who felt better about the whole exchange—she or we.

The little girl who asked me how to die posed a question I don't know how to answer. I'm far from sure that I myself know how to die. But I do know that I still fear death. I fear its mystery.

Two things more than any others concern me now when I think of my own death. One is that I want to have enough lucid time, at the end, to say a few last words to Wanda. I have no idea what those words will be, but I know their meaning: that I love her, that I'm grateful I found her, that our years together were the best ones of my life. I don't want to be cheated of my good-bye to my family; I want to be able to say it.

The second thing that concerns me is more difficult to speak about. That is the pain of cancer and the possibility that I will be reduced, at the end, to a living death. I'm not sure how much pain I can tolerate. And even more importantly, I can see no reason to go on living if I am no longer able to think for myself.

But my feelings are not the only ones that seem to me to be relevant to this question. It involves the whole problem of death with dignity and the further problem of euthanasia. Everyone wishes, for himself and those he loves, that their end will conform to one part of the dictionary meaning of euthanasia: "an easy death." Certainly, such a death is a profound blessing for everyone.

It is the second part of the definition of euthanasia that poses moral and ethical problems. The *American Heritage Dictionary* phrases that part of the definition in this way: "the action of inducing the death of a person for reasons assumed to be merciful." The nature of that action is, of course, the crux of the problem. Injecting a lethal dose of a drug into a dying person induces his death—induces it for reasons of mercy. But it is also an act of killing. I would shudder to give over to anyone —physician or layman—the power and the responsibility to commit an act as grave as that. However, there seems to me a real difference between injecting a lethal drug into a dying patient and letting that patient die naturally, without the benefit of life-prolonging drugs or heroic measures. I see no merit in keeping someone alive for a week or two when that person is comatose and has no hope of recovery and when it requires complicated, expensive machinery, intravenous feedings, and all kinds of other paraphernalia just to keep his vital signs going. The medical skill and the expense that such heroic measures involve would seem to me far better put to other uses—to speeding up the search for the causes and cures of cancer and to reducing the mortality rate among newborn babies. We owe it to life to put our best energies into conquering its enemies—the diseases that cut life short and that snatch it away just as it has begun.

The nineteenth-century English poet Arthur Hugh Clough expressed my feelings far better than I ever could myself:

> Thou shalt not kill; but needst not strive
> Officiously to keep alive.

FIVE

February 26, 1975—Orville Kelly Day.

The phrase had a pretty nice ring to it. Make Today Count is more than a year old now, and I thought I was pretty well accustomed to the fact that I've become something of a celebrity—no longer the plain private citizen I'd always expected to be. But I'd never before had a day named for me. This would be a first.

What pleased me even more than the simple fact of the honor was the auspices under which Orville Kelly Day was being held. My hosts were to be a group of high school students in Macomb, Illinois. Their concern and interest seemed to me to be especially significant, a demonstration that people are beginning to hear one of the primary messages that Make Today Count is trying to get across: that our society must change its attitudes toward death and dying; that we must bring this fact of life out into the open so that we can deal with it in a more humane and understanding way. And if this change is to take place, it must begin with young people—young people who have learned to accept the idea of death and who, therefore, will be able to bring up their children, from the beginning, to understand that death is part of life—a part of life we do not have to like, but that we *do* have to face realistically. The young people who were running Orville Kelly Day, like the college students I've been speaking to all over the country, are real pioneers—pioneers in teaching the rest of us how to face death and dying honestly, and how to live life well. Of all the rewards that Make Today Count has brought me, the greatest has been to see the interest of the young in its message.

For a while, it was touch and go whether I'd get to Orville Kelly Day at all. I had awakened that morning feeling terrible. I had caught a cold several days earlier, and it had been getting progressively worse. It was winter; the temperatures in the Midwest were near freezing; and it had snowed several days in a row. The night before, I had taken the long drive to Donaldson, Iowa, to speak to a church group. Which had apparently made matters considerably worse: When I went to the hospital that morning for a blood count, the doctor found that the cold had gone into my lungs.

"You really should stay in bed," he told me. "I'm afraid it may turn into pneumonia."

His prediction turned out to be correct. I *did* develop pneumonia. The next day, I went to bed and stayed there for nearly two weeks. But I wasn't about to accept his prognosis when he made it. I *had* to be at Orville Kelly Day. For my own sake, and for the sake of the students who had planned it—the members of an English class which had been studying death and dying since the beginning of the school year. According to their instructor, Rosemary Randolph, the kids had been preparing for Orville Kelly Day for more than a month. How could I possibly disappoint them? They had even sent information about the event to the local radio station, and it had been announced during news broadcasts the previous day.

I had already been to Macomb High School once before, during the previous year, and had spoken at an assembly. The students and I had hit it off extremely well. They seemed to be interested, and that made it easy for me to talk to them. I had not thought that high school students—all of them healthy, none of them suffering from any kind of serious illness—would want to tackle such difficult issues as the emotional problems of cancer and death. When I was in high school, such subjects were never even mentioned. But these kids seemed to have realized that Make Today Count is as much about life as it is about death, and they accepted my presence quite easily. (Not, as I subsequently discovered, that they were completely open with me. These were the youngsters I mentioned earlier—the ones who sent me letters after my appearance, indicating there were some questions they'd wanted to ask, but were too embarrassed to bring up.)

Now we were crawling along in my car at about twenty miles an hour on the way to Macomb. There were three of us—Wanda and I and Jeanne Kuster, a young woman who came to work with us soon after Make Today Count was started, and who handles all the organization's secretarial responsibilities. Jeanne was driving, and having a hard time with the icy back roads and the fog that was clinging to the windshield. The highway would undoubtedly have been easier going, but we were late, and it had been my not-too-bright notion to take the back roads as a shortcut.

I hadn't told Wanda what the doctor had said at the hospital that morning; I hadn't even told her I wasn't feeling well. It was a violation of my own philosophy; but in this case, I didn't care. Anyway, I really didn't have to tell her. She could see that I was feeling sick, and she had pleaded with me all morning to cancel my appearance and get into bed. But I wasn't going to give up my day. Although now I was beginning to regret my decision. I felt just terrible. I was coughing, and my lungs burned so badly that I wanted to pull them out and throw them away. And even though we had the heater on in the car and I was bundled up in a sweater, an overcoat, and a scarf, I could feel the cold slicing through me like a knife. What's more, I was tired, and just about everything irritated me.

"I'll bet you've got a fever, Kelly," Wanda said, handing me the thermometer she's learned to carry with her when she's out with me.

I felt pretty sorry for myself as I sat there with the thermometer beneath my tongue. I had hoped so much that I could get through the winter without a cold. The previous year, I had caught cold several times, and I had to be taken off my chemotherapy drugs. Those drugs are my lifeline, and I didn't like the idea that I might, once more, have to stop taking them. Now, all I could think about was getting back home, crawling into bed and staying there for a month of Sundays. Then I remembered we'd scheduled a Make Today Count chapter meeting for that evening. Well, at least I wouldn't have to go out again, once we got home. The meeting was to be at our house.

I pulled the thermometer from my mouth and examined it. "What the hell does this thing say, anyway?" I asked Wanda.

She hadn't been able to find our new thermometer that morning, and she'd had to take an old one from the medicine chest. It had measured our children's fevers through so many cases of mumps, measles, and colds that the numbers on its scale were barely visible.

Wanda peered at it. "I'm not sure," she said, "but it's above normal."

"Thanks," I snapped. "That's a big help. For crying out loud, you know we need to have a decent thermometer. That's the first thing you'd better do when we get back to Burlington. Buy a new one."

By now, Wanda has become used to what she calls my "crankiness." She knows it's a sign I'm feeling rotten and discouraged about everything, and that it has nothing whatever to do with my feelings for her.

"Don't worry, Kelly," she said. "When we get home, I'll buy one. After I've put you to bed."

"You won't have to put me there. I'll do it myself. And we'll try to leave here early. I'm sure the kids will understand."

We were about a half hour late when we pulled into the high school parking lot. I could see immediately that the kids were going all out. Right in front of the main door was an empty parking space with a big sign: *Reserved for Orville Kelly.* Just the sight of that sign made me feel better, and once we got inside the school, I almost forgot how sick I felt. Two students were waiting for us in the lobby, the boy holding a corsage of yellow roses for Wanda, the girl holding a white carnation for me. And there was a hand-lettered sign above the door: *Welcome back, Mr. Kelly.*

Mrs. Randolph hurried forward to greet us. A small woman with gray hair, she has an expression that clearly shows her strength and determination and tries—unsuccessfully—to conceal her inner sweetness. She probably would be the last one to put it in such sentimental language, but it's obvious that she loves her work and she loves her students. The class on the study of death was her idea—an experimental project she thought of after my first appearance at the school and that required, I'm sure, a lot of explaining to get approval for. Classes on death and dying are not exactly traditional fare for high school students.

"Mr. Kelly, we're so glad to see you," she said. "We were beginning to get worried."

"We were late getting out of Burlington, and then I stupidly suggested we take the back roads to save time."

"No problem. It's Orville Kelly Day all day here. Let me take you to the library. That's where the main ceremonies will be. I can't tell you how much the students have been looking forward to this. The library isn't big enough to seat all the kids who wanted to hear you. We had to turn away about a hundred who'd put in requests to come."

Over the door to the library, as we approached it, I could see another sign: *Your Adopted School Welcomes YOU.* That really touched me. When I'd been at Macomb last time, I'd been so pleased by the kids' warm response that I'd told them I'd like to adopt every one of them. They hadn't forgotten. I stopped for a moment to catch my breath and noticed my shoelace had come undone. Here I was—a guest of honor—and I couldn't even keep my shoelace tied. What's more, I couldn't even bend over to tie it for myself. I felt like a little boy as Wanda knelt down to tie my shoe for me.

The library is a large, hexagonal room, with a high ceiling that makes it look even more spacious than it really is. The winter sun shone through the windows like a spotlight, focusing on the center of the room, where chairs had been placed for Wanda and me. Each of the walls had its own sign: *Orville Kelly Is OK; Make Today Count; Welcome, Mrs. Kelly.* Wanda wiped her eyes when she saw that one.

As we sat down, the students began to enter. By

the time they had all arrived, there were more than two hundred of them seated at the back of the room.

A madrigal choir was first on the program. Sixteen students—the boys in black suits, the girls in black blouses and white skirts—came in from a side door and sang two songs in their clear young voices. Next came the gifts. First, a certificate of honor for me for coming to the school; then an honorary editorship of the high school newspaper; then a key to the school; and finally a diploma: I was now an honorary graduate of Macomb High School, presented with my diploma by the principal himself.

"Mr. Kelly has come here as our very special guest today, and we're proud to be able to show him how special he is to us," Mrs. Randolph said as she introduced me. "My class has planned a special luncheon for him and we have a few added surprises, but first we have a list of questions we'd like to ask him. The list was drawn up by the whole class, so it represents the things we specially want to know. You can answer some of the questions or all of them, or none of them, Mr. Kelly. You're an honorary graduate now, so you can do anything you want. And we know you're fighting a cold, so we don't expect you to talk too long."

Cold? Who had a cold? I was fine now. My face

felt a little hot and flushed, but that was from the excitement and the warmth of the occasion, not from my cold.

"I have to apologize. I'm never speechless, but I'm having trouble with my lungs now, and it's a little difficult for me to speak. But I *do* want to tell you how proud I am to be the recipient of all these gifts. As soon as Wanda and I get home, we're going to make a place of honor on the wall of my den for this diploma."

That pleased them, I could see. But I still found it hard to believe that when we got to the serious part of the day's events, they would be able to understand the things I said. The development that pleased me most about the public response to Make Today Count—the interest that young people have shown in it—still remained the one I could least understand.

"If you want to ask the questions now, Mrs. Randolph," I said, "I'll try to answer them."

She glanced at a sheet of paper in her hand. "Do you feel that most people waste their lives?"

"I don't know whether *most* do. But I'm afraid that many people *do* waste the time they have. It seems to me that people should do the things they want to, and should be the kinds of people they want to be. The most pathetic souls I've met are the ones who are unhappy with their work and the way they live their lives, but are afraid to make any changes in what they do. Life is very precious, and no matter how much time one has to live, it goes by very quickly. You really begin to realize that when someone has told you your time is limited; when that happens, you make up your mind to do the best you can with the time you have left. And when you do that, there can be all kinds of unexpected spin-offs, as I found out. If I hadn't made up my mind to do what *I* wanted to when I got sick, there'd be no Make Today Count today. It started, after all, from a simple piece I wrote for my local newspaper. And I wrote that piece because I *wanted* to."

My audience was completely silent; their expressions solemn.

"When you talk about dying, you're really talking about living. How do you make people aware of this?"

"Each person has to become aware of it his own way. One of the toughest is the way I learned it: by being informed that I was terminally ill. I had to accept the fact that I was dying—the fact that death comes to all men, including Orville Kelly. Once I accepted that, I could start living again."

"How do you stay cheerful and keep your sense of humor?"

"I don't always keep my sense of humor. I've been pretty irritable lately. Wanda can tell you that.

But I know it's important to try to keep a sense of humor. When you lose the capacity to laugh, you've lost the knowledge of how to live."

Suddenly I remembered something. I'd forgotten to take my medication. I reached into my pocket, pulled out my pillbox, and downed my pills. It was late; I should have taken them earlier. I felt a stab of panic, but forced myself not to worry. One of the things I've learned the hard way, since my cancer was discovered, is that the human body is not only terribly vulnerable, it's terribly tough. And it's just as destructive to live every moment in frightened self-protection as it is to live in complete defiance of all the rules of health.

"You recently attended a seminar with Dr. Elisabeth Kübler-Ross. Could you tell us something about that?"

"Dr. Ross is the author of a very important book —*On Death and Dying*. And she is a real pioneer. She's one of the first physicians to have made it her business to *listen* to people who are terminally ill—to find out how they feel and what they need. Those are the first things our society needs to know if we're to deal with death and dying in a humane way.

"The seminar that Wanda and I attended was made up of professional people and cancer victims, and the idea was for each group to learn from the other. I think we both *did* learn. And, by the way, it was a lively event. But the best part was spending an evening with Dr. Ross and her husband, just chatting and listening to music. That was relaxation. And you need some relaxation after talking about death all day."

The questions went on. How did I meet Wanda? How was Make Today Count doing? Why did so many doctors have such a hard time telling patients about terminal illness? What was my favorite subject when I was in school? That one was easy: "It wasn't mathematics, I can tell you that."

The kids laughed; apparently we had something in common.

"English was my favorite. I loved to read, and I loved to write. I even won a national contest, for writing an essay entitled 'Why I Would Grow Flax on My Father's Farm.' We weren't living on a farm then, and I didn't even know what flax was. But that didn't bother me. I read up about it, and then I went ahead and wrote."

We could all laugh at that, too. It seemed a good note on which to break up our meeting.

"Thank you again," I said to them, "and I hope that the sun shining through those windows is shining in your hearts."

The kids all stood up, applauding wildly. A standing ovation for a dying man—I was touched beyond words.

❧

Next we were rushed off to a local restaurant, where we were luncheon guests of the members of Mrs. Randolph's class. Again, the kids showered me with gifts—a varsity letter award for sports; a school pennant; a school button; a car sticker; a plaque with the picture of each student in the class. This was not just another day that counted. It was something very special to me. I kept repeating the words "thank you" over and over and over again. They were the only ones I could find to say.

Far more important than their tribute to me as an individual was the seriousness with which the students had approached their course work. They gave me a copy of the booklet that summed up their project. It was called "A Study on Death," and the preface described its purpose: "to develop a realistic point of view toward death," and "to examine its biological, social, cultural, spiritual, economic and psychological aspects." The kids really *had* examined the subject. They had conducted interviews with an attorney, a priest, a coroner, an insurance company representative, and a funeral director. They had written pieces on their reactions to some of the field trips they'd taken—to a funeral home, a cemetery, and a crematorium. One of the girls had written an essay on the way she wanted her own funeral conducted. She wanted the services to be held in her own living room; she wanted the guests to wear their everyday clothes, and not to dress in black. And she hoped that before she died, she would have time to write personal notes to each of her friends, to let each of them know she had accepted the imminence of her death.

I invited the students to Burlington for a barbecue at the Kellys', and by the end of the luncheon they were thinking of ways to rent a bus for the trip. They just couldn't stop themselves. They laughed, they joked, they were full of life. It was death that had brought us together, but it was life that we were celebrating.

As we were getting into the car for our return trip, one of the girls handed me an envelope.

"It's a letter, Mr. Kelly," she said. "Maybe you'd like to read it on your way home."

After we'd gotten out of the city, I took the envelope from my pocket and opened it.

"Dear Mr. Kelly," the letter read. "As one of the students at Macomb High School, I can say that you have truly been adopted here. I can identify with you. You've put a new light on things I've thought for years. You may not understand a word of this note. What I'm trying to convey to you is a feeling —and feelings don't fit into words very easily. You have made life a little easier for one student. She understands a little more now, and hopes for a little more understanding and hope in her life. I was once blind, but now I see."

The letter was unsigned.

And suddenly I saw, too—I saw one of the reasons I had found such interest in Make Today Count and in the dying man who started it among high school and college students. Because young people are especially sensitive. Because they know they are standing on the threshold of their lives—because there are so many things they want to do, and hope to do, that even an infinity of time doesn't seem to them to be enough. Because they care so much about life—so much that they are open to terrible depressions as well as to great joys. Because they see so many adults walking around numbed and apathetic—just going through the motions of living—that they have begun to believe that only people whose lives are in jeopardy can love life as much as they do.

When we got home, I went straight to bed. But although I was exhausted, and my cold had come back full force, I was too keyed up to sleep. And those kids reminded me of my own youngsters—for whom I'm not just a dying man, a kind of symbol of the value of life, but a flesh-and-blood father, whom no one knew about when he was healthy but who suddenly achieved a kind of fame when he got desperately sick. I worry about my children—about how life looks to them now, and how it will look to them when I'm no longer here.

Mark, for example. He's fourteen now—just at the stage where he wants to be independent. There are ways in which my illness has encouraged his independence, but there are other ways in which it has pulled him back further into the family than perhaps he likes. And, because he's the oldest, he will probably remember all our problems more clearly than any of the others. I hope he respects me, but sometimes I'm afraid he sees me only as a weak, dying man, and it makes me angry to think he is being cheated of a healthy father.

Mark doesn't take much interest in Make Today Count; perhaps that's one of his ways of preparing himself for the future. But he has accompanied me on a few of my speaking engagements. We drove to Kentucky together once, and on the way we stopped several times along the highway to look for old beer cans. For some reason, he collects them, and there are more than a hundred in our basement. When I was a kid, I collected baseball cards. The collecting mania seems to be part of growing up. And at least Mark is helping to clean up some of the litter.

Because he was my first child, I've always had a special kind of protective feeling about Mark. Even now, I have to fight to keep myself from protecting him too much. Last winter, he hurt his leg playing basketball, and it had to be put in a cast. One day, as I was driving down to the grocery store, I saw him limping along on his cast, trying to keep up with two of his friends. From the expression on his face, I could tell he was in pain. I wanted to pick him up and offer him a ride in the car. But I forced myself not to. It would have embarrassed him. "Besides," I said to myself, "he has to learn to be a man. Every boy has to learn it. And I'm not likely to be around to help as long as most fathers."

I worry about Lori, too. Of all our children, she's the best student; the only one now in school who seems really to enjoy reading and studying. I'd like to see her go to college, if she wants to. But among the ways I avoided facing death before I became ill was to fail to take out an insurance policy. If Lori wants to go to college, she'll have to do it on her own.

Lori is ten now; last year, she wrote a composition for her class that I still read now and then:

"Well, it all happened when I was seven or eight. My dad had cancer. He had to go to Iowa City for his treatments. At first I didn't know he was going to die. But as days went past, I was feeling scared. Then he started a meeting for people called Make Today Count. He meant you don't just sit around and wait to die. Make each and every day count. I was so worried. I loved him very much and I didn't want him to die. So, every night I ask God to try to heal him. This is what I say:

"'Dear God, thanks for the many gifts you have given us. And dear Jesus, my Dad has cancer and if you could please heal him, dear Lord. I love you very much and I love my Mom and Dad very much.'"

By 7:30 that evening, fifteen people were sitting crowded around our dining-room table. We don't ordinarily have Make Today Count meetings in someone's home, but we thought that we would try an experiment this time, to make the meeting even more informal than it usually is. It's never easy to talk about death; the more relaxed the setting, the better things are likely to go.

I usually preside over our meetings in Burlington, but tonight I hoped that the other members would carry the ball most of the time. A reaction was beginning to set in after the emotional high of my experience with the students: I was exhausted, and my lungs were bothering me. My body would probably have felt better if I'd been upstairs in bed. But my spirits would have been worse. To me, the most important part of the entire Make Today Count program is our meetings: only there can we share our problems with others whose lives have been touched in some way by incurable illnesses. Even though it takes time to build people's confidence and get them to participate, it's well worth the effort and the time. The future of Make Today Count is in these meetings. When the time comes that I have to curtail my schedule, the meetings will be the last thing I'll cross off the list.

Most of us in the room were old friends, but as I looked around, I saw a few strangers. The oldest friends were George Riordan and his wife, Myra. The Kellys and the Riordans have grown very close since Make Today Count started in Burlington. Three years ago, George learned he had bone cancer; at the time he was diagnosed, he was given two years to live. But George is an Irishman, and a hard-fighting Irishman, at that. Although he is now confined to a wheelchair, he has already outlived his doctor's prediction by a year. He's fifty-five now, and still plans to die of old age. Myra is a dear woman, who has supported her husband in every way, and is as much a part of Make Today Count as he is.

Next to the Riordans were the Paxtons—Maxine and Fred and their daughter, Kerry. Kerry is sixteen, and she has leukemia. Her features are plain, but her long black hair makes her beautiful; it seems to reflect the slightest ray of light. Kerry has accepted her illness—by which I mean she knows how sick she is, but she's fighting her illness with every ounce of her strength, and is living every moment of her life. She has become a real missionary for Make Today Count among young people. Fred Paxton, her father, was a busy and successful insurance salesman, but he went into semi-retirement when Kerry's illness was diagnosed, so that he could have more time to be with his family.

Craig and Susan Jensen are both in their late twenties, and they have two children—a boy of two and a girl of four. Craig still has trouble dealing openly with his feelings and with his illness—lung cancer—but he's trying hard. And Susan is a real help.

Cindy, a nurse, is a regular at our meetings, driving each time from Iowa City, where she works in University Hospital. This time, she had brought her boy friend, Larry, a medical student I'd never met before.

The Reverend Bill Jackson, another Make Today Count regular, had called me the previous day to ask if he could bring a guest to tonight's meeting.

Her name, I discovered, was Nancy Caldwell; a young woman in her early thirties, she had recently lost her husband to cancer. At the opposite end of the table sat a couple I'd never met before. They introduced themselves as Wallace and Cora Doyle —"an interested couple," as she put it.

With so many of us in the dining room, it seemed much smaller than usual. But closeness has its advantages. It makes it hard for people to be stiff and tense. Even though we would soon be discussing some pretty depressing subjects, the atmosphere was loose, almost jovial.

"You should have seen those kids," Wanda was saying. "They were something else. They even gave Kelly an honorary diploma. I think I'm jealous. I never even got one diploma, and now Kelly has two. Maybe we can have the name changed on one of them, to turn it into mine."

"You're getting to be a real celebrity, Orville," George said. "Can I have your autograph?"

"Why not?" I answered. "That and twelve cents will get you a pack of gum."

"I think I'd rather have some beer," George said, and chuckled.

I looked at my watch. "I guess it's time to begin now," I said. "We don't have any formal agenda for this meeting—no speaker, or anything. But before I throw the floor open for anything anyone wants to say, I wondered if we ought to talk about our next meeting. Does anyone have any ideas about what we should take up? Shall we have a speaker? We've had lawyers, ministers, and doctors as our guests. Who would you like next?"

There was silence for a moment. Then Cindy spoke up.

"How about a psychiatrist?" she asked. "He might have some good ideas about how to deal with the emotional problems of cancer. And he might learn something from the people here, too. If you think it's a good idea, I could try to get hold of someone through the hospital."

We all nodded in approval.

"Good, I'll look into it tomorrow, then," she said. "And one other thing I'd like to bring up. The other day, a man with cancer was admitted to the hospital. He's not married and he doesn't seem to have any relatives or friends in Iowa City. I spoke to him today, and I think he'd like to have someone to talk to. I know it would make him feel a lot better."

Hospital visits have become Wanda's specialty. She knows as well as anyone that hospitalized cancer patients often need someone just to hold their hand or listen to them, and whenever she can, she goes to the local hospitals to visit cancer patients. Wanda has a way about her that draws people to her. She's tender-hearted—which explains, I guess, why we have so many cats and dogs around the house. So I wasn't surprised to see her volunteer for the task.

"I'll go too," said Myra Riordan.

"Good," said Cindy. "That will make him feel much better, I know."

"Well, what would you like to talk about tonight?" I asked. "I've got a cold, but we didn't come here to talk about that. We're not here to talk about any of our medical problems; we're here to talk about our feelings. But we're not here looking for pity. Anyone who is, is in the wrong place. Understanding, yes. And help, yes. But pity, no." I paused. "I might as well say the words 'cancer' and 'death' now, so we won't be afraid to use them the rest of the evening. We've got to be open with each other, our families, and our friends. Make Today Count means sharing."

My words were greeted with the awkward silence I've learned to expect at the beginning of our discussions. Everyone around that table was concerned about something—everyone had a personal problem that needed to come out in the open. But no one wanted to be the first to speak. I've seen this reaction time and time again.

At the end of the table, I could see Mrs. Doyle squirming and pursing her lips. She obviously wanted to speak, but she was having a difficult time working up the nerve.

"I—I'd like to know something," she finally said, her voice cracking. "Let me pose a hypothetical case. What about a situation where a person finds out he has cancer, but his children have grown up and moved away? The children have their own children and their own problems. Why should it be necessary to tell them? Wouldn't that just add to their burdens?"

"No, I don't agree with that at all," I said. "We have to bring cancer out in the open and face it. If the children are mature enough to be told, they should be told—"

"But," she interrupted, "but what if the children are living far away, say on the West Coast. If they found out, they would just feel guilty about being so far away from their parents. And since there's nothing they could do to help, it wouldn't be fair to them."

I looked at her directly. "I still can't agree with that thinking. When I told my family—"

"But, Mr. Kelly," the woman broke in. She was determined to fight. "What good would it do to tell them? Wouldn't it just hurt them?"

I had seen that kind of insistence before. She was pushing her "hypothetical" case too hard. It wasn't hypothetical, at all. It was actual. Either she or her husband had cancer. I knew it. We were up against that most powerful enemy: the fear of speaking out, the fear of hurting others—the fear that actually represents a refusal to face the truth. But if we don't face the truth, if we keep ourselves in ignorance, we've lost the power to fight back against the cancer; the power to fight for our lives; the power to find hope.

"When I told my family," I started again, "we all became closer than we had ever been before. Wanda and I could start talking to each other again. We didn't have to hide anything from each other and I didn't have to tell the kids to leave the room so I could speak to their mother. We all decided to spend as much time as we could together and to enjoy one other. We didn't tell Britty, who was only four years old at the time, because we thought he was too young. But he found out, anyway, through our nine-year-old daughter, Lori. One night I was lying in my bed, resting, and Britty came up to me. 'Are you going to die of cancer?' he asked. I was surprised by the question, but I told him, yes, I probably was. Then he pointed up to the sky and asked if I was going to go up there or if—and he pointed to the ground—I was going to go down there. I told him I wasn't sure, but that after twelve years in the army, I thought I had friends in both places. I'm sure he didn't really comprehend what I was talking about. He's still too young to understand what cancer means, but at least he isn't being shielded from the truth."

Mrs. Doyle was shaking her head. But I wasn't about to give in to her. I couldn't tell her what she wanted to hear.

"The other day one of Lori's friends asked her if her father was going to die of cancer. Lori said, 'Yes, he's dying, but he isn't dead yet.' What that means is that I'm learning to live with cancer, and my family is learning to live with it too. My cancer is as much their problem as it is mine. And it's a problem for the children of the person you're talking about, also, even though they may not know, yet, that anything is wrong. That person isn't going to be able to die without the children knowing. Think what grief they'll feel *after* the funeral, knowing they didn't help their parent when he was alive."

I paused for a moment to see if anyone else was going to speak. There was silence. It was time for the big question.

"Tell me, Mrs. Doyle," I spoke softly, "do you have cancer?"

No response. She glanced at her husband, and he looked at her. She looked down at her lap and pulled a handkerchief from her purse.

"Yes," she whispered, "I do. I have cancer."

"Have you told your children?"

"No—I haven't."

"I remember when George found out," Myra said. "When he finally told me, I thought the world had stopped. I didn't know how I'd be able to go on. But we have two children—a son and a daughter. They both live in Illinois now. I wrote them telling them what was happening. Just putting it down on paper to my children was a big help to me. I was able to say things to them I couldn't say to George. And they've been such a comfort to both of us."

Mrs. Doyle listened intently. Myra and she are about the same age, so Myra's words had a real impact on her.

"One of the first things I found out was that I couldn't face cancer alone," I said. "Thinking constantly about cancer and dying can be pretty depressing. Cancer can be a barrier between us and the outside world. That's why so many of the letters I get from people with cancer mention suicide. Those people are lonely. They have no one to talk to. Many of them don't think life is worth coping with any longer. But that's not true. Life is the only thing we've got, and it's worth coping with all the time. Cancer patients aren't dying each day from cancer, but living with it. You can't enjoy cancer. I can't think of one good thing about it. But you can live with your husband and children. You can enjoy them, and they can enjoy you."

"I even have little talks with my kids now and then to keep them informed of what's going on," Wanda said. "Kelly gets cranky sometimes, and sometimes the kids forget the reason—that he has cancer. It's hard for them, so I have to keep reminding them, 'Your father is on medication and it makes him upset. But he really doesn't mean it. He still loves you.' The kids' feelings get hurt, sometimes, but they eventually understand. If they didn't know what was happening, they'd never understand at all."

The conversation was beginning to generate its own steam. One of us had a problem, and the rest of us were going to try to help. The Doyles were still upset and somewhat resistant. But now that the problem had been brought out into the open, the rest of us were more relaxed. And eager to help.

"Mrs. Doyle, if I could say something for a moment? I'm Kerry. I have leukemia, and I found out the hard way. I had been feeling pretty terrible, and I'd been to the doctor, and I knew something was wrong. But I didn't know how wrong. The doctors and my parents kept telling me that they weren't sure what the problem was. All they said was that I needed more tests."

Kerry looked at her parents. They were staring down at the floor.

"I tried to keep going to school," she continued,

"but I got so sick it just didn't work out. One day I found a letter from my aunt to my mother and father. It was open, so I read it. The first sentence was: 'I'm sorry to hear Kerry has leukemia.' I couldn't believe it. I read it four times. The letter said 'leukemia.' It said I had leukemia, and I didn't even know it. I was mad, real mad. Why hadn't my parents told me? After all, it was my life, wasn't it? I had a right to know, didn't I? I rushed into my parents' bedroom and asked them why they hadn't told me. They both froze for a moment and didn't say anything. Then they explained that they were just trying to protect me; that they wanted to do what was best for me.

"At first, I couldn't understand that, and I was furious at them. But later, when I thought about it, I could see how they felt. I thought then, and I still think, that they were all wrong. But I *do* understand how hard it was for them to speak to me.

"The point I'm trying to make, Mrs. Doyle, is that you can't keep that kind of information away from people. Chances are that others will find out in some offhand way, just as I did. Finding out that way is so much worse."

Both the Doyles were looking fixedly at Kerry, listening to her every word.

"I heard of something the other day that proved to me how absolutely correct we are in Make Today

Count when we say that people should be open about cancer. There's a small children's hospital in California where most of the patients have leukemia. They're kids, about my age. They all know what their problem is, and they're all told everything about their medical treatments—what the purpose is, what the side effects may be—everything. What's more, there's room at the hospital for their parents to live, so that the families can be together. So the kids, their parents, and the doctors are a real team—equal partners in fighting for the kids' lives.

"I don't know how many of those kids will make it—just as I don't know whether I will. But all of us are living our lives now, not dying them. The morale of those kids at the hospital is absolutely marvelous."

Maxine Paxton blew her nose and wiped at her eyes. Make Today Count meetings can be draining, sometimes. A comment, a particular word, can trigger a flood of emotions. But the tears disappear quickly, as the conversation continues. Now Maxine was remembering her own struggle when Kerry's illness was diagnosed. She had wanted to tell her daughter, but she couldn't bring herself to say the words. She had convinced her husband that they should remain silent.

"Your situation is the reverse of ours, Mrs.

Doyle," Kerry's father said. "You're the one who has the cancer and doesn't want to tell your family. But after what we've been through, let me tell you, Mrs. Doyle, you can't keep it inside. You wouldn't be here if you could. I'll bet if you called your children tomorrow and slowly and gently explained to each one what your situation was and what it meant, they would understand, and they would thank you for telling them."

Mrs. Doyle's husband put his arm around her. She was shaking, trying to hold back the tears. But she couldn't; the dam burst and she began to cry. These were tears of relief, though. She had finally told someone her problem. She was beginning to break the barrier.

"I see your point," she mumbled. "I don't know if I can bring myself to talk to them. The doctors seem to be optimistic about treatment. I'll have to try, I guess."

"I've got bone cancer," said George. "I've had a hell of a time just trying to stay alive. And then my son-in-law—my son-in-law . . ." his voice quavered for a moment as he tried to regain his composure. "My son-in-law committed—he committed suicide. He was only twenty-eight. Our daughter is only twenty-five, and they have two young children. He just went out into the backyard and shot himself in the head a couple of months ago. He never said anything to anyone. He—he—he must have gone through more torture than I've ever gone through. But no one knew what made him do it. He never confided in any of us. If we had known, maybe we could have helped. It kind of makes you wonder why God lets these things happen."

He stopped for a moment. We were all silent.

"When I first found that I had cancer, I thought I would never be able to talk about the way I felt to anyone—not even to Myra," he continued. "But she forced me to come to one of these Make Today Count meetings, and I realized that I should try to talk. Blaming God wasn't good enough anymore. I finally started talking at the meetings, and to Myra, and everything got much better. I even began talking about arrangements with my brother-in-law—he's a funeral director. Oh, by the way, if any of you needs to contact a good funeral director, I can give you his number."

That broke the tension. Everyone laughed. A little nervously, but we were laughing. When things quieted down, I spoke again. Mrs. Doyle should hear from Craig. He was another who had had trouble speaking openly about his illness.

"Craig," I said, "at the beginning you had the same problem I had. You, too, had trouble talking to your family."

"Yeah, that's for sure," Craig said. "In a way, I

still have the problem. I still find it tough to talk about cancer with Susan. I don't want to upset her. She has enough to do with the kids."

"Mrs. Doyle, I knew Craig had cancer and he knew it too. But it took us the longest time to talk about it—for him to say anything to me." This was Susan. "I was so glad when he did because by then I was starting to go nuts. I knew something was wrong—something more than his illness—but I didn't know what it was. I was scared and confused. We had been very close before, but now we were growing away from one another. Sometimes I wanted to explode, but I couldn't quite do it."

Wanda was an expert in this area. I had put her through a lot.

"I know what you mean, Susan," she said. "Nights were the hardest for me. I would try to go to sleep, and all these things would come into my mind. I would see Orville lying in a casket, and I had thoughts of suicide. I didn't want to go on without him. I imagined myself going to his funeral and then taking a knife and stabbing myself through the heart. I even had thoughts of crawling into the casket with him and being buried in his arms. I just loved him so much, and I felt so helpless. . . ."

Wanda's voice always cracks at this point in the story. I've heard her tell it several times, and each time she falters at that point. She won't admit it, but she still has to fight her horrors occasionally. But she fights them and she wins.

"It got to the point where I didn't want to be away from him," Wanda continued. "I wanted to spend all the time I could with him. It seemed important to be with him every minute because I thought I was going to lose him that very day.

"I remember going to the hospital in Iowa City. It's a big hospital, a university hospital, and you get lost in the shuffle. Nobody means to make things tough, but that's what happens. People just didn't talk to me. We would be sitting there, the children and I—I didn't have a baby-sitter to leave them with—and they would get so bored in the waiting room. They couldn't see their dad and their dad couldn't see them. I didn't know which way to turn. People would go by, and they would stare at me. The nurses were busy running here and there. They didn't take time to say anything. Gee, if somebody would just have come up and said something like, 'Mrs. Kelly, can I help you? Can I do anything for you? Do you need a friend, someone to talk to?' I just felt completely abandoned. I thought I was the only one on God's green earth who was going through something like this.

"And now, by being open about it, we have such an appreciation for life. Little things mean so much to us. And we try not to waste any day. When we get up in the morning, it's a beautiful day, whether it's sunny or raining. We enjoy the simple things in life. And we grew close again. We could even talk about funeral arrangements. I'll never forget the day I opened the mail and found a eulogy that a minister had written for Kelly. I didn't know Kelly had asked him to write it, and he wasn't around when the mail came in that day. I sat down and read it two or three times before I could accept it. It said, 'Now that Orville is dead,' and went on. It's not easy to read your husband's eulogy when you expect him home for dinner that night. But imagine what it would have been like if I had read the letter, and Kelly hadn't told me he was dying. I think I would have had a heart attack."

"I feel a little ashamed of myself when I listen to you talk, Wanda," Craig said. "But I'd like to spare my family a few things."

"It's in your approach," I said. "You can be open without destroying others. You can't walk into the room and say, bluntly, 'Honey, I've got cancer. I'm going to die.' You have to be compassionate. You can sit down with your wife and say, 'Honey, I think there's something we should talk about. It's going to take a while, but I think you should know about it,' and go on from there."

I think Craig knew by now most of what I was saying, but it was worth repeating. He still needed encouragement to be open. By this time, I also knew we should get Nancy Caldwell involved. She was young, but although her face still showed traces of the vibrancy it must once have had, it was drawn and lined. Being a widow was not easy for her.

"Mrs. Caldwell," I said, "the Reverend Jackson told me you wanted to come this evening. You must have something to say."

She spoke hesitantly. "I have a problem I don't seem to be able to resolve by myself. It's been about five months since Jerry died. We both knew he was dying, but we tried to live with it. But now that he's gone, I don't know—I just feel so alone without him. And worthless. I work part-time, and I have to look after my ten-year-old boy. But I seem to have lost all my friends. About two months after Jerry died, I attended a meeting for young wives, and one of the women said to me, 'I didn't expect to see you out so soon.' Do they think I should retire from life now? Then another woman called to invite me to her house one afternoon, and she made it very clear to me that her husband wouldn't be there. I'm not after her husband. I just want to have the same friends I had before Jerry died. I don't want to be expected to mourn month after month, year after year, until I'm eighty years old. When I'm around people, they seem to cringe when I bring up Jerry's name. It's as if we should all try to forget him. But I don't *want* to forget Jerry. I can live my life and still remember him. Yet whenever I try to relate a story or happening from the past, I'm told I don't have to talk about it."

Nancy reached for the minister's hand and grasped it tightly under the table. She had promised herself that she wouldn't cry, and until now she had kept that promise.

"But what bothers me more than anything," she continued, "is that I need to be needed. My boy looks so much like Jerry that I sometimes think of him as an adult. I know he's too young to be expected to do the things Jerry could do, but I can't help myself. I—I don't know. I hate feeling so useless. And so lonely."

Wanda was looking thoughtful. She was, I knew, putting herself in this woman's place—just as she had put herself in the place of the woman whose husband had died on that Virgin Islands cruise. She knew that Nancy's anguish would be her anguish one day.

"I have already felt a little bit of what you're going through," she said in an understanding voice. "I've been thinking a lot about what it will be like when Kelly's cancer gets worse. I'll have Make Today Count to be involved with when he's gone, but it will still be difficult to live without him. Even now, I miss him when he goes out on speaking trips.

Sometimes I think I'll never be able to get along without him. But when I get to feeling like that, I think how long I've had *with* him. I've had more than fourteen years. You had more than ten, Nancy. It could have been much less. Or none at all. We can be thankful for what we've had. And that doesn't mean we have to live in the past.

"And I've promised myself one thing. I will not rob my children of their childhood because their father is dead. They can't be expected to be adults, and I think you're realizing that."

"Time has a way of healing most wounds," I added. "That's probably not too comforting right now, but it's true. Part of the problem you are facing is society's problem. Friends don't like to be reminded of death because it makes them uneasy. It reminds them that they will die someday. So they try to avoid such situations, and they avoid you. There are a few other widows in Make Today Count whom I think you'd like to meet and talk to. I'll give you their telephone numbers later."

"Really, Make Today Count people are so beautiful," Wanda said. "I love them all. I have a list of all our Burlington members upstairs. If I'm blue and need someone to talk to and Kelly's not here, I just get my list out and call the special person I would need at that particular time. These people are practically my family."

The group had reached a certain peak, and I knew it. It was time to start on the journey down.

"You know, sometimes I wonder who benefits more from these meetings—those with cancer or those who are healthy," Reverend Jackson said. "I seem to be learning a lot from you people just by listening. It's sometimes hard to explain to people how important life can be. I see and feel your sorrows, and I see your desire to cope with them. I wish I could make all the members of my church feel the same way."

Cindy's friend Larry had been sitting quietly all through the meeting. He represents the kind of person I hope Make Today Count can reach. He's learning to be a doctor and he has never had any personal experience with death. But he is going to have to deal with it once he gets out into practice. I hope Make Today Count can help him understand the emotional problems of the terminally ill.

"I want to thank you for letting me sit in on your meeting," Larry said. "We've just begun seeing films in my class on dying patients—we even have a film of you and Mrs. Kelly. But it doesn't sink in as much when you examine it in a classroom. I guess my professor was right when he said that our present attitudes toward death are like the attitudes we had toward sex fifty years ago. Sex was a taboo subject of discussion then; death is a taboo subject now. I'm still scared when I think I'm going to have to talk to terminally ill patients in the hospital. But I think I'm better equipped now that I've been here with you than I was yesterday."

"But it's not always easy to know what tactic to take with cancer patients," said Cindy. "Cancer patients that I've known always wanted to be in control of themselves and their lives. But each person reacted differently to the stages of dying. I've learned to check with the patient to find out what's important to him. For one person, it may be the control of pain. For another, it may be the finishing of unfinished business. I'm still pretty new at nursing, and I haven't seen that much death, and sometimes I have the impulse to push my feelings on the patient. If I think a person would *want* to be alone, I have the impulse to leave the room. But really, that person might want to have someone there. What we nurses have to do is lessen a person's isolation and fears, I guess, to help him concentrate on the things in life that are important to him."

"You know, Cindy, I've always wondered what the world would be like if suddenly everyone knew at this moment when they were going to die," I said. "I would think it would be a pretty messed-up place. I guess it's better not to know. But I find so many people who suffer the agonies of death before they actually die. They go through the grief of the funeral before the funeral ever happens.

"I just want everyone in this room to realize that we all have something in common. We are all of us alive. That is a fact. We have to take advantage of our lives, of the time we have left. We were all born to die; in that sense, we're all terminal. Those of us who are sick have to have simpler goals now than when we were healthy. But we can still have goals. I told Wanda the other day that I wonder sometimes how much longer I can go on feeling optimistic knowing that in the end I will lose the battle. Then sometimes at night I'll go out to the back porch and sit down on the couch and look up at the moon and stars. The vastness of the sky makes me feel small and insignificant, but it reminds me that I'm a part of life and that life is precious to me.

"The business at hand is the business of living. That is the secret of Make Today Count. That's what those kids at Macomb have found out. You have to want to live. If you give up, or cover up, you've died, even though you're still living. Make Today Count is so simple. We can't take time for granted. If we try to make each day count, our lives will have meant something for us and for our families."

I was exhausted. Although Make Today Count

meetings rarely last longer than an hour, they are intensive sessions. I was pleased with the way this meeting had gone. I felt a sense of hope—hope that we in the room had accomplished something together. We had all participated. But my feeling of hope also came from the knowledge that we were still fighting and trying. Trying to make each day count. We in that room were friends, perhaps the best friends we ever had. We were sharing. And we were alive.

"Why don't we get some coffee now?" I asked. "And some coffee cake. Unless there are some more comments or questions?"

Everyone shook his head.

Until the next month, the meeting stood adjourned.